CW00382416

THE LONGEST WALK

THE LONGEST WALK

The World of Bomb Disposal

PETER BIRCHALL

ARMS AND
ARMOUR

Arms and Armour Press
An Imprint of the Cassell Group
Wellington House, 125 Strand, London WC2R 0BB

Distributed in the USA by Sterling Publishing Co. Inc.,
387 Park Avenue South, New York, NY 10016-8810.

British Library Cataloguing-in-Publication Data:
a catalogue record for this book is available from
the British Library

ISBN 1-85409-398-3

Designed and edited by DAG Publications Ltd.
Designed by David Gibbons; printed and bound
in Great Britain.

Illustrations are from the author's collection or are
reproduced by courtesy of the Royal Army Ordnance
Corps and the Royal Logistics Corps.

CONTENTS

CONTENTS

FOREWORD
by Brigadier R. Rook, OBE

I am delighted that, at long last, a history is being published that covers the specialist work of those members of the Army Ordnance Corps, the Royal Army Ordnance Corps and, since 1993, The Royal Logistic Corps, involved in the Army's ammunition profession. The reader will follow the evolution of this profession over the last hundred years, gaining an insight into both the routine work of the officers and soldiers charged with care of the Army's ammunition as well as their higher-profile activities related to bomb disposal.

The history goes into many different aspects of the profession, its practitioners and those who support them, but, regrettably, some facts and interesting anecdotes have had to be left out for security reasons. Nevertheless, it is a very full history and one that is excellent testimony to diligence and extreme bravery displayed throughout two world wars and many other campaigns besides. It is also a tribute to members of the ammunition profession past and present who, I believe, epitomise all that is best in the wider profession of arms.

PREFACE

Every technical expert, military or civilian, knows the destructive power of an explosive device, be it the conventional service bomb or shell or an improvised explosive device, manufactured by a terrorist in some back room. No matter the development of equipment to aid the technician in his work, at some time an approach and then physical contact must be made with the destructive item that he has been tasked to either destroy or make safe – the longest and loneliest walk ever undertaken. By this time he will know the approximate size of the device and once the approach starts, he will know that at a certain distance he is safe; then at a point some injury would be inflicted if the device explodes; a bit further and he can expect serious injury; past this point and the fear of a life terribly injured soon passes in the now certain knowledge of a very quick death in the event of an explosion.

In some cases, especially with terrorist devices, the first walk results in the placing of the disrupter in the hope of immobilising the device. There is then the agony of a second long walk: has the disrupter worked as planned, or is the device now more deadly?

A bomb disposal expert's work is described by many as 95 per cent total boredom and 5 per cent sheer terror, but for many the terror factor is experienced at a far greater frequency than can be reasonably expected – for some, during a tour of duty, many times a day. Remember – the false alarm is the real device until the very last minute.

This book is dedicated to all those who ever made the longest walk and especially to those who never made the return trip.

I am indebted to so very many people for the time and information that they have willingly given to me over the eight years it has taken for me to complete this book. Most of them I cannot identify but some I can; my sincere thanks to you all.

Major General J. A. Hulme, Director General of Ordnance Services in 1989, who first approved of the project; Major General L. T. H. Phelps, for permission to use extracts from his recent history of the Corps.

Brigadier M. C. Owen for permission to use extracts from the *Corps Gazette*; Brigadier John Sharland, who kindly provided my initial contacts; Major Bert Gracie for his help over the years; and, finally, to Brigadier Roy Lennox and Brigadier Richard Rook, who helped me to finish the book off.

Others who have given invaluable assistance are, Captain W. W. F. Chatterton-Dickson; Lieutenant Commander Dan Nicholson, Royal Navy; Squadron Leaders David Lloyd-Roach and Peter Barker, Royal Air Force; Doc Knight, Royal Air Force; for his early comments, Lieutenant Colonel M. H. H. Brooke and Captain Nick Moody, Royal Engineers; Brigadier P. D. Wickenden and Lieutenant Colonel S. W. Thompson, Royal Army Medical Corps; Deputy Chief Constable David Howe and Superintendent Bill Kerr; Stasu Labuc for her psychometric testing and encouragement over the years, Peter and Sheridan Gurney for their friendship. Thanks are due to the very many members of the Royal Army Ordnance Corps for all their contributions, their photographs and anecdotes, some retired, others still serving; H. D. McCormack, Joe Chamberlain, Howard Cripps, Stan Simpson, John Anderson, Mick Atkinson, Andy McRae, D. Townsend, R. T. Dallen, Mark Wickham, Steve Harmon, Paddy McCreanor, Kevin Callaghan, Norman Bonney, Ken Underwood, Andy Hawkins, Willie Munroe, Peter Woodhall and Simon Wilkinson.

Special thanks to David Langham for his considerable research help over the years, to my staff for typing, retyping and draft reading: Gill, Lisa, Joan, Carole and Liz; and to my wife for listening to all the stories for many years, for providing the cartoons and drawings and finally, following the loss of a computer disk, sorting out and retyping the entire work over Christmas 1996. Her admission that it was quite readable made my day!

CHAPTER 1

INTRODUCTION

We have all heard about explosions, not only in Northern Ireland but as a result of terrorist activities all over the world. Nearer to home there was the dreadful Lockerbie air disaster, the result of a bomb on an aircraft. There have been a number of similar horrific incidents in England. The IRA bombing of the Officers' Mess of the Parachute Regiment in Aldershot: five innocent women mess workers died. The bomb on the bus on the M62 carrying soldiers and dependents: 12 dead. The bomb in the Tower of London, little children with injured faces and limbs blown off: one dead and 37 injured. The Birmingham pub bomb: nineteen dead and 120 injured – a horrific incident in a crowded public house, eye witnesses reported on the busy bar, suddenly a terrible flash, people flying through the air, bits of people, legs, arms, clothing, furniture. First the silence then the screams of pain, young people fighting to get out. The smell of the smoke, the fear and chaos. For those present, a never to be forgotten nightmare; for the rest, no real comprehension of what it was like.

For many, these incidents are so much a part of everyday life, especially for those in Northern Ireland. Reports on television tend to be limited to a few words, unless it has been a major incident, then a short bit of film. They never show the real horror. Remember – if someone is killed, someone else has the job of collecting the bits together for burial.

The effects of any explosion can be the same, be it due to a terrorist incident or to chemical substances or gas. An explosion is, in very simple terms, a rapid expansion of gas which produces a shock wave with a build up of pressure. Normal air pressure inside or outside the human body is approximately 15psi. If this is increased by as little as 5psi then your ear drums perforate; increase normal pressure by 15psi and you are dead. Your lungs collapse. The waves of energy and force created by an explosion will enter your mouth and other openings and totally destroy you. Limbs and flesh will be torn off and in extreme circumstances very little will remain, and all will be scattered over a very wide area.

These facts are given, not to dramatise, but to simply explain the terrible and gruesome effects of an explosion. All those who deal with explosives know the results of a mishap yet they continue to complete their tasks, coolly, calmly and professionally, be it a terrorist device, an unexploded war-time bomb or the simple disposal of unserviceable ordnance.

Definitions of the Responsibilities of each of the Services

The 'Bomb Squad', 'Bomb Disposal', letter bombs, incendiary devices and the Anti-Terrorist Squad, together with the IRA and other organisations, all these are well known to us all, and regrettably known throughout the world in one form or another.

The purpose of this book is to tell of the people who are involved in dealing with explosive devices; their selection and training, their duties and responsibilities. It will include not only the Royal Army Ordnance Corps in Northern Ireland but also the Royal Engineers during the Second World War and subsequently, the Royal Air Force and the Royal Navy. However, the major part concerns the Royal Army Ordnance Corps from the early Laboratory Foreman of 1895 to the modern Ammunition Technician of the 1990s; from the disposal of surplus war stores from the Boer War, the First and Second World Wars to the Gulf conflict. It will cover the training for routine duties and specific duties which include Northern Ireland and some of the more unusual and hazardous duties undertaken and little publicised. Although the great variety of postings of the 1950s era has been reduced with the granting of independence to our colonies and protectorates, the life of the Ammunition Technician continues to be interesting and demanding. It can include routine depot life in the UK and Germany, overseas in Canada or the Falklands, on detachment to the Middle East or on active service in Northern Ireland.

In the interest of national security, and to protect those who have been involved in action against the terrorists in Northern Ireland, it is not possible to name individuals in a way which can lead to their identification. For the same reason it is not possible to describe the technical nature of the terrorist device. Who knows who might use the information; it might be a schoolboy or an anarchist? The evolution of the bomb from the first black sphere with sizzling fuze, to the highly sophisticated electronic long delay time bomb, is a fascinating subject, and a book on the subject would no doubt be a bestseller, such is the demand in this troubled world. Things were different not so many years ago when, if you were awarded a decoration for valour, there was a detailed citation of the event, similar to those included in this work. To protect the brave men of today the citations are regrettably brief ('for gallant conduct whilst undertaking EOD operations in Northern Ireland') showing the need to protect for a long time into the future. It is my earnest hope that at some time someone will be able to make a record of the men and the details for the benefit of future generations.

The reader who is not familiar with the true function of the Ammunition Technician will be aware of the 'bomb disposal expert' and the 'Bomb Squad'. Neither of those terms are accepted within the armed services. The term 'bomb disposal expert' was first used to describe those members of the Royal Engineers who, during the Second World War, actually dealt with aircraft bombs which the German air force dropped in such quantities on the United Kingdom. It was a perfect description of what they did: bomb disposal. The expression was given great publicity from 1970 to describe Ammunition Technicians of the Royal Army Ordnance Corps in Northern Ireland and these days there is a great deal of confusion in the mind of the general public as to who does what and why.

Firstly it is necessary to explain that it is not possible for anyone to join any of the services to become a bomb disposal or explosives expert. There simply is no single trade that specialises in this work. The responsibility for which of the services deals with incidents involving explosive devices is also confusing as is the type of incident.

To explain the niceties. The basic terms in use in the services are Explosive Ordnance Disposal (EOD) for conventional munitions and Improvised Explosive Device Disposal (IEDD) for others. The former is the destruction of manufactured items which contain explosives which are of a military or commercial type. The latter, IEDD, is the disposal of illegally produced items of an improvised design, individually made, frequently using strange explosives of a not particularly effective type and normally produced and used by terrorists.

The duties of the various armed services in the United Kingdom may be clarified as follows. The **Royal Navy** is responsible for all items in or on the sea or on the shoreline below the high water mark. Their experts are Clearance Divers by training but they are also experienced in dealing with all types of explosive devices. The **Royal Air Force** deal with their own aerial bombs and ammunition on their own air bases and involving crashed aircraft; their experts are from within the general trade of Engineering Technician (Weapons). The **Royal Engineers** became involved in 1940 with German aircraft bombs due to their training and experience with demolition explosives and mining and tunnelling techniques; their experts are now all Combat Engineers first and bomb disposal experts secondly. The Royal Engineers deal with all battlefield clearance work and all aircraft bombs and projectiles which have penetrated the ground. The **Metropolitan Police** are responsible for the area of London within the M25 boundaries. They employ, as civilians, former members of the RAOC who were licensed Ammunition Technicians and who choose to leave the Army and continue their hazardous duties. Perhaps these officers are now amongst the most experienced, in their terrible trade, anywhere in the world.

The above seems logical and simple; life is never really like that. For example, the Royal Engineers have trained divers who deal with explosive objects in lakes, rivers and canals. The Royal Navy can deal with land service ammunition if it is in the sea. All services receive specialised training in dealing with terrorist devices (IEDD). This training is nowadays given by the Royal Army Ordnance Corps at its training school, and although the RAOC have teams available throughout the UK to deal with all types of incidents, the Royal Navy, the Royal Air Force and the Royal Engineers contribute some teams trained and licensed by the RAOC to deal with IEDD, excluding Northern Ireland. The RAOC is responsible for clearance of all IEDD in Northern Ireland and the technician is specially trained and licensed for his operational duties.

The most important first step in tackling an EOD incident is to determine its priority. In 1982 a formal reshaping of the responsibilities of the Royal Army Ordnance Corps (RAOC) and Royal Engineers (RE) was made by the Ministry of Defence. Although in practice this protocol had applied for over ten years it was felt necessary to formally lay down the guide lines. The RE and RAOC both have separate and differing capabilities to undertake Explosive Ordnance Disposal (EOD) mainly stemming from the necessary allied skills; in the case of the RE, mines, demolitions and earthmoving in peace and war. Their specialisations for EOD should either option exist were defined as:.

Royal Engineers lead in:

a. Clearance of aircraft bombs, mines and military booby-traps. However RN and RAF have their own special fields of expertise.

b. Excavation or approach clearance to a device, up to the point where it is located and identified.

c. EOD Search, except for electronic counter measures to identify or combat a radio-controlled device.

d. Area clearance.

Royal Army Ordnance Corps lead in:

a. Clearance of land service ammunition.

b. Clearance of terrorist and home-made bombs and explosive devices of an unusual nature.

c. Incidents where forensic evidence is required.

d. Situations where the risk of detonation is unacceptable, unless the device lies clearly within the field of expertise of RE or another service.

In 1987 NATO felt it necessary to classify EOD incidents according to their potential threat.

Category A: Assigned to EOD incidents that constitute a grave and immediate threat. Category A incidents are to be given priority over all other incidents, and disposal operations are to be started immediately regardless of personal risk.

Category B: Assigned to EOD incidents that constitute an indirect threat. Before beginning EOD operations, a safe waiting period may be observed to reduce the hazard to EOD personnel.

Category C: Assigned to EOD incidents that constitute little threat. These incidents will normally be dealt with by EOD personnel after Category A and B incidents, as the situation permits, and with minimum hazard to personnel.

Category D: Assigned to EOD incidents that constitute no threat at present.

The Character of the People who 'Do the Job'

What do all these men have in common? The ability to stand stress and at the same time to retain a high degree of effectiveness is frankly a prerequisite of men and women who are required to make major decisions, be it in the services or in civilian life. A study of the qualities required of management in business emphasises the ability to command, but also a person requires good judgement, a logical and decisive mind, the ability to learn quickly from previous situations, self confidence and prudence, the ability to communicate and personality which commands respect. Finally, and obviously, he or she requires technical ability in the work to be undertaken. Yet there is no certainty that a person with all these management skills would make a bomb disposal expert. In addition a person needs to be self contained yet not introverted; in being decisive great awareness is necessary that there is a risk to life and limb, not only to the operator but to others around him.

Even if it were easy to list the ideal person, anyone who has ever interviewed staff will know the reality. A salesman who cannot sell himself is useless, but having sold himself at the interview can he then sell the product? Some people can gain qualifications with ease, but can they put theory into practice? In explosive ordnance disposal the operator must have the ability to assess a situation for what it is and then be decisive in rendering it safe, often when the clock is running against him. He may even have to walk up to the device to render it safe. This is the quality that cannot readily be assessed. He must be prepared to perform these tasks without much prior warning, frequently every day, even several times a day for days on end. Imagine the stress, imagine the adrenaline, imagine having to move into this hazardous environment. Most people would find another job.

The pages that follow aim to indicate to the reader what the job is all about. They do not cover the normal activities of any of the trades or arms of the various services. They deal mainly with the disposal of explosives, with one or two asides to try and add a touch of the broader picture. Although they are concerned mainly with the work of the RAOC, they aim to show how each arm of the services fits into the overall scheme, and how their activities have developed to the present high level of effectiveness. There are duplications and many omissions which will be obvious to the 'expert'.

The Royal Army Ordnance Corps is responsible for the safe storage and handling of all types of land service ammunition, including the repair and serviceability of these stores. Another of the duties of its personnel is the safe disposal of ammunition when it has reached the end of its useful working life. Due to their breadth and depth of knowledge of all types of ammunition and explosives, following an extensive and comprehensive training, they now deal with all conventional explosive ordnance disposal and most improvised explosive device disposal. This is the only arm of the services in which the Ammunition Technician is exclusively trained in dealing with explosives. A technician would normally spend all but a small part of his military service in other more 'safe' and routine activities [than coping with terrorist devices]. He is, however, unique since he is the only serviceman to serve continuously throughout his career dealing with explosives.

This is not to say that the routine duties of the Ammunition Technician do not at times involve a high degree of risk. After the last war there was a massive amount of ammunition in store, a considerable amount of this had been produced to manufacturing standards below those required prior to the urgency of the war, much had become damaged and dangerous. One example was the examination and disposal of 40mm Bofors ammunition where the alloy fuse had simply rotted to dust leaving the striker and spring exposed to the slightest knock. Another was the 25-pounder fuse that deteriorated and produced crystals of cuprous azide highly sensitive to friction. As this ammunition was still in use, especially in Korea and Malaya, all fuses had to be removed, a dangerous job performed by ammunition examiners working alone in special 'blast proof' work bays.

There were similar problems with other ammunition. There was the ammunition in Malaya where the fabric bag containing the propellant had rotted due to the adverse climate conditions. A gun cannot be loaded with handfuls of propellant which, incidentally, looks like spaghetti, so all condemned charges had to be destroyed. The disposal procedure was to lay the bags of propellant out in long rows, cut them open and then burn them. There was a considerable tonnage to be burned and this went on day after day in the tropical heat. It had to be laid out, burned and the area wetted down to avoid premature ignition, then the procedure started all over again.

The following passages from *In Danger's Hour* by Douglas Reeman perhaps convey what it feels like to deal with a 'beast':

> Sherwood saw the sappers paying out a field-telephone line while they waded through the shallows, pushing the boat ahead of them. Once the tide began to turn it would be too late yet again. As he held on to the boat and sloshed through the water with the others, Sherwood tried to remember everything he had learned about this type of mine. Packed with over fifteen hundred pounds of deadly Hexamite. Enough to knock down several streets, or demolish a cruiser.

A sapper switched on one of the lights, and Sherwood could imagine the consternation on the shore. It was so close it was startling, lying half-submerged, the torn parachute vanishing into the shadows of deeper water. The mine was cleaner than usual because of the sea. The one he had dealt with before had been grimy with black filth from the exhaust smoke of the plane which had unloaded it. He could see the identifying letters and figures shining in the hard beam, the way it appeared to roll about in the current. But that was only a trick of the light – otherwise he would be dead.

'All right Sergeant, take your chaps off now.' The men moved back into the surrounding darkness.

Sherwood felt the sea breeze like ice on his face. He had tried to make it sound encouraging for Wakeford's sake. Twelve seconds. Maybe. But here the difference was that there was nowhere to run, no empty house, or garden wall, or as in one incident, pressed against a railway embankment. That one had exploded and he had seen two complete railway carriages fly over his head as if they were paper kites.

He tested the telephone. 'D'you hear me, Stinky?' He made himself chuckle, although he felt as if the breath was being strangled out of him.

'Yes sir.'

'Write this down. It's a type seven. That's the only classification we have to go on so far.' He measured it with his eye, moving the light an inch at a time until the beam was shining beneath the slopping water. 'About nine feet six long, I'd say.' He paused to tug his bag clear of the water on to a small hump of sand. The sea sounds seemed so loud out here. The tiny purr of the fuse would probably pass unheard. Not that it would make any difference anyway.

'I've found the fuse.' He fumbled for his special callipers, the ones he used to prevent it from moving and coming to life. He wiped the spray, or was it sweat, from his eyes. The callipers locked on to the keeping ring which held the whole fuse in position. Sherwood rocked back on his heels. 'There's something wrong.' He did not realise he had spoken out loud.

'What is it sir?'

'Not sure.' He peered into the water again. Was his mind playing tricks or was it already deeper?

'It's too easy, Stinky. All I have to do is unscrew it, just like the earlier models.'

Wakeford said, 'Be careful, sir.'

Sherwood smiled despite his raw nerves. Careful. Commander Foulerton had died trying to defuse one of these mines. He was a true expert, a professional. Otherwise, this mine might indeed be one of the easy jobs. Lucky to have been washed clean by the sea, to have come to rest the right way up.

Sherwood moved slowly along the mine, his free hand feeling it as if it was alive. He returned to the fuse again and touched the keeping ring with his fingertips. A few turns, and the whole thing would slide out. Not easy, but not impossible.

It was then that his hand began to shake as if he had a fever. He put the light on his bag and gripped his wrist with the other hand. For Christ's sake, not now! He tried again. If they were on dry land, he would risk attaching a tackle to the hoisting flaps. As if to mock him the wind ruffled his hair, and part of the sodden parachute floated against his thigh like a shroud.

There was no more time. His whole body was quivering. This was what he had always dreaded more than anything.

He picked up the lamp again and began another careful inspection. A voice seemed to jeer at him. You're putting it off. It's over. Why not give the brute a kick and end it all right now?

He tried to cling to fragments of memory, like a man caught in a dying ship's final whirlpool. Her voice on the telephone. When was it, one, two hours ago. Was that all?

He pulled out the special spanner he had had made for himself at Vernon. Foulerton had probably used the original one.

He stared wildly at his flickering reflection in the water. 'Hoisting flaps' It seemed to scream out at him so that he almost dropped the lamp.

He spoke carefully on the field telephone. 'Stinky. This mine has hoisting flaps. They stopped using them eighteen months ago.'

'I don't understand, sir?'

'Don't try, old son', he recalled his words to the Canadian Major in Sicily when Ransome had run to the stretcher. 'Just pray!'

He lined up the flap with the fuse, tightened his spanner around it and then stared at the low clouds.

Twelve seconds. He put his weight on it. Nothing happened at first, then it scraped away from its new paint and began to turn.

He gasped, 'It's under the flap, Stinky.' He let the lamp fall into the sea by his boot, which had now filled with icy water. Another turn, and another. How much time would he have to know what was happening?

He shouted, 'It's here, under the flap. I'm doing it now'. He inserted the callipers and began to turn. Suppose Foulerton had seen it too, and this was the real booby-trap.

He yelled, 'Well, it's too bloody late now, you bastards.'

The fuse slid into his fingers, and the sudden silence seemed to probe his ears like fingers. He returned to the original ring and inserted the callipers. Inside the gap there was the second fuse, now made harmless by his discovery. But for some warning instinct the mine would have exploded at the first or second turn of the keeping ring.

He heard Wakeford calling, 'Are you alright, sir? Please answer me.'

He bent over against the mine and gasped into the telephone, 'come and get me out of this – I – I can't move.' He vomited over the telephone and hurled it into the water.

Men were running through the water towards him, then someone put his arm around his waist and a voice shouted, 'Here, lend a hand. The poor bastard's done his bit for the night.'

Then there was Wakeford on the Chesil Beach, although Sherwood did not remember how he got there. It was no longer empty, but dark figures ran and bustled in all directions.

Commander Bliss reached out and took his hand. It was like a piece of ice.

Bliss said, 'I wondered what you chaps did. Now that I know, I'd still like to be told how you do it. That was a bloody brave thing you just did.' *

All EOD operators were connected by radio to their number two: in the days of the Second War this was by field telephone. They were required to carry on a running commentary of what they were dealing with and the exact sequence of operations. If they were killed then the next operator knew at what point the first went wrong. The last recorded words of some have been, 'Oh my God what's this ...' or 'Oh bloody hell what's this ...' – a sobering thought, professional to the end.

The foregoing indicates the stress that was experienced during World War Two, when dealing with unexploded aircraft bombs and mines. Similar stress is an everyday part of life for the expert in Northern Ireland, the UK mainland and other troubled parts of the world.

Some individuals continue to serve the public after leaving the armed forces. There are a handful of retired RAOC experts now employed by the Metropolitan Police responsible for all incidents in London. During October 1981 there was a series of incidents in London. A device was found in Wimpy's in Oxford Street and an operator was sent to the scene. As he was examining the package it exploded and he was instantly killed. Another device had been located in Debenham's and an operator was tasked to deal with this. As one device had exploded, it was a certain bet that the second was no hoax. One device had killed a highly experienced officer, so it was necessary for the second operator to examine the scene to see if it was possible to identify any new anti-handling or other 'booby-traps'. Now, small groups of men in a dangerous occupation tend to become very close; a special friendship and companionship develops. This operator had to examine the dead body of his friend, traumatic for anyone, and then deal with the bomb at Debenham's. Ken Howarth was awarded a posthumous George Medal and the second operator was also awarded the George Medal for his brave conduct, which resulted in the Debenham's bomb being made safe.

* Reproduced by kind permission of the author and the publisher, William Heinemann Ltd.

During the course of my research I have come across many interesting items, some still covered by security classification. However, there have also been a number that I can include, and the following gives an interesting insight into the immediate pre-war period of 1939, a time when many people realised what was about to happen.

Ammunition Bulletin No.1 was issued in May 1939 when, to many, the war seemed a serious possibility. The interesting references are in sections 44 to 49, 'German Bombs'. I wonder if the author would still class the anti-personnel 'Butterfly' bomb as presenting no serious problem! I have little doubt that those who followed, dealing with bomb disposal during the war, would take issue over the general tone which implies 'no real problem'. Perhaps too many believed then that the war would be over in a matter of weeks or, at most, a couple more months.

44. German Aircraft Bombs.
The following data on German Aircraft Bombs is circulated; it is not entirely complete, but will be helpful to those called upon to deal with unexploded Bombs.

H.E. Anti-personnel.
These are not likely to be used over towns as they are intended to burst on impact. There are two types - the S.C. 10 and S.C. 10t; the former has vanes, the latter has not. The S.C. 10t is intended for low flying attacks on personnel and has an 'allways' fuze with short delay action, on impact, for the protection of the aircraft. The S.C. 10 has a Direct Action fuze.

The low flying bomber must use the S.C.t bomb with a 2 second delay fuze, and troops exposed to this form of attack are given some little opportunity for taking cover by reason of the delay action.

H.E. General Bombardment Bombs.
These are most likely to be used in the attack on towns, factories, etc. They are fitted with the Rhinemetall electric fuze. This fuze may be set (a) for direct action (b) short or long delay, ranging from 10 seconds to 168 hours, or even longer; or (c) it may comprise a booby trap, designed not to burst the bomb on impact, but only when an attempt is made to move it afterwards. So far as is known the external appearance of the fuze is the same for direct action, delay or booby. The fuze or fuzes are placed in the side of the bomb, one fuze being used with the 50Kg. bomb, two fuzes with the heavier bombs.

As the fuze or fuzes are placed in the side of the bomb and electrically actuated there is no necessity to obtain direct impact in order to cause them to function.

The disposal of such bombs, if unexploded, is clearly attended with grave risks on account of the likely existence of delay and booby trap devices.

Incendiary.
Bombers of the Heinkel III type can carry 8 canisters each containing 15 incendiary bombs of the G.C. 50 type, i.e. 120 such bombs per machine. A larger quantity of the smaller incendiary bombs can be carried though the exact number is not known.

The Incendiary bomb also contains a quantity of explosive for the purpose of discouraging the attention of the A.R.P. personnel.

Gas Bombs.
The only bomb known of this type is the G.C.10 which is similar in external form, length and construction to the S.C.10 for Anti Personnel previously described. The H.E. charge is omitted, and a gas container

inserted, the same type of fuze being used. There are numerous reports concerning other gas bombs and gas spray but no further precise information.

48. General.
Unexploded Bombs of the Anti Personnel, Incendiary or Gas types present no serious problem regarding disposal, and any experienced I.O.O. can deal with them on the general lines laid down in any R.A.O.S., Part II. Incendiary bombs should be collected and disposed of by burning in some isolated spot. Care should be taken to avoid starting grass or forest fires and not too many bombs should be burned at the same time. The burning ground should be surfaced or cleared of grass for a radius of 50 yards at least, and it should not be used for the disposal of H.E. or Gas Bombs. Gas Bombs should be dealt with by trained Anti-Gas personnel fully equipped with the necessary protective clothing, etc.

Unexploded Bombs of the H.E. type present a very definite problem owing to the probability of long delay fuzes and the possibility of booby trap devices being used. If the bomb lies in open ground it should be disposed of where it lies. In view of the delay action, it would be preferable in such cases to mark the position and place a sentry near the spot, i.e. in a dug-out at a suitable distance, and leave the bomb there for 10 days. Don't move it then, in view of possible booby traps, but carefully complete the arrangements laid down in Regulations and blow it up in situ. Sandbags should be piled round the bomb and care should be taken to ensure that its destruction is assured at the first attempt. If the destruction of the bomb lying in the open is likely to affect important drainage, water, gas, electric or other supplies, it may be found preferable to defer its destruction, the spot being patrolled, or otherwise protected. The reason for suggesting this course is the difficulty of ascertaining whether a delay or booby trap is fitted. If the former, the bomb could be removed after 10 days, but risk of the latter precludes this action. If the bomb is not in the open, the above considerations are aggravated and the best procedure to adopt must be deduced from a careful consideration of all relevant circumstances. A number of experiments are in hand with the object of finding a solution to this problem.

49. Information.
The vital necessity for the efficient functioning of the services connected with the destruction of unexploded bombs is information. All that is available to date is contained in the preceding notes. If the complete demobilization of Key industries, due to the risk of a large unexploded H.E. bomb being a booby trap, is to be avoided, we must avail ourselves of every possible bit of information likely to throw light on the type of fuze actually in use. If it can be established that an unexploded H.E. bomb in a large machine shop, departmental stores, etc. is actually a non-delay, non booby trap type, its removal for disposal elsewhere becomes a reasonable proposition. Again, if it can be established that a delay fuze is fitted, it may be possible to establish a clear area for 10 days, and arrange for the removal at some risk of valuable articles. A greater risk may be faced in very special and exceptional cases by the immediate removal of the bomb, but this course should not be attempted without higher authority.

To help in the solution of these difficulties all details of enemy bombs obtained by military personnel should be sent immediately to C.I.A. who will collate and circulate them through the medium of these Bulletins for the information of' I.O.Os and Ordnance Officers generally. Early information of this kind may be the means of saving life, as the handling of unexploded H.E. Bombs is a risky business.

An interesting and initially overlooked fact was that most German equipment and fuzes were patented in the United Kingdom, 'to protect the manufacturing rights'. In the early days, no-one thought to check the records in London.

CHAPTER 2

AND IN THE BEGINNING

The Army Ordnance Corps came into being under this name in 1896. The first record of experts on the establishment was in that year, when one laboratory foreman was listed. As this is a record of those who trained and served as ammunition examiners and Ammunition Technicians, and as the origins of the trade started with laboratory foremen, it is only fitting that reference should be made to the first of the many.

The Army Ordnance Corps' Seniority Roll of 1896–1900 shows only two laboratory foremen:

2315 Sergeant T. W. Kettle – Promoted sgt in 1896 and shown on the roll as a dual tradesman, labourer and laboratory foreman. Originally he was noted as a corporal and only a labourer. Promoted to staff sergeant on 13 September 1899 with the trade of Laboratory Foreman. He regrettably died of disease during the Boer War, at Bloemfontein, on 8 June 1900. He was entitled to the Queen's South Africa Medal, a first for the trade, recorded in 1896 on the Seniority Roll.

2481 Staff Sergeant A. F. Miles – Promoted staff sergeant as a laboratory foreman on 1 March 1900; previously he had been recorded on the roll as a labourer, whilst serving as a sergeant. Upon promotion to warrant officer class 2, squadron quartermaster sergeant (WO2, SQMS), he was shown in the trade of clerk, although this was not unusual in those days when all warrant officers class 1, conductors and sub-conductors were classified as clerks. There is a little more available about the career of Captain Arthur Frank Miles, born 28 April 1873. He passed through the ranks of the Corps and was promoted conductor in November 1912, commissioned as a lieutenant in October 1914 and promoted to captain in October 1917. He was an ordnance executive officer 2nd class in March 1920 and retired in February 1928. His service included the South African War, Gallipoli and Egypt, and he was awarded the South Africa Medal, Queen's one clasp, King's two clasps, 1914–15 Star and Victory Medal, with a Mention in Despatches, and the Long Service and Good Conduct Medal.

Back in time, 1681 to be exact, reference is made to a laboratory located in Woolwich, and in 1746 an order was made whereby the controller, fire-master and other staff be appointed to ensure the art of making fireworks, for real use as well as for triumph. The Corps as a definite military unit, with enlisted privates and officers who received their commissions from the Sovereign, subject to military law and discipline, and the obligation to wear uniform, did not exist until after the Crimean War.

It was with the end of the Boer War that the Army Ordnance Corps was first officially involved in the disposal of large quantities of ammunition, either dangerously damaged or not of service pattern. These explosives were destroyed by either blowing up or by 'drowning at sea'. The extent of the work can be gauged by the fact that it occupied between two and three years. The pattern for the future was established.

An early article in the *Army Ordnance Corps Gazette* of November 1908 recalls:

> It was, of course, impossible to convert to any peaceful purpose the high explosive shell that was found desirable to remove from service, and therefore such accumulations had to be destroyed out of hand. A long series of explosions were carried out at the Ordnance Depot, BLOEMFONTEIN. The larger shell is that of the 9.45 inch Howitzer, the weight of the shell is 260lbs and its explosive charge is a black powder resembling the mixture employed in our older type projectiles. The smaller projectiles inter spaced between the 9.45 Howitzer are high explosive 6 inch and 4.07 inch shells weighing 100lb and 45lb respectively. The bursting charge is Lyddite of highly explosive properties when compressed or confined. The smaller projectiles are a mixture. The charges employed for this, as for any other disruptive purpose in the Military Service, is Gun Cotton.
>
> In the series of explosions carried out at BLOEMFONTEIN, a pit 20 feet square by 20 feet deep was dug out on the VELDT about two miles from the Ordnance Depot and three miles from the town.
>
> The heavier shells were placed at the bottom of the pit, above these were laid the smaller projectiles and the slabs of wet gun-cotton, in one of which was inserted a dry primer with electric detonators. On top of this mass were placed sand bags filled with damp earth to 'tamp' the explosion and increase the detonative effect. The block house was about 800 yards away.
>
> On pressing down the handle of the exploder, a miniature inferno ensued. Its concomitants were a thick column of smoke about 500 feet in height by 200 feet at its greatest breadth, in which the greenish yellow fumes of the Lyddite were plainly discernible, and a deafening roar which shook the doors and windows of Bloemfontein and at the opening of the series, shattered the nerves of the worthy citizens who, after recovering from the first shock, looked anxiously at their clocks and watches, thinking that the noon gun had fired and that all time arrangements had been dislocated (what a gun).

> The local disruptive effects were evident by the fact that the shells were shattered and that most of the debris was covered by the mass of earth that filled the bottom of the pit. A considerable number of fragments mainly from the smaller projectiles and the head of the 9.45 inch shell, were hurled from the pit in all directions, falling 2000 yards from the scene of the explosion.

That was in 1900. After the First and Second World Wars the same efforts continued, in very much the same way; the only real change was the amount destroyed at one go, and the increased distance from an inhabited area.

The first recorded Army Ordnance Corps laboratory operation also occurred during the Boer War, Captain Partridge and Armourment Staff Sergeant Bird evolved the Kroonstad flare, effective but primitive. This was a lead ball on a trip wire which when disrupted dislodged a brick which in falling fired a friction tube which in turn set fire to a few strands of cordite leading to a bag full of waste fabric soaked in kerosene. This created a loud bang to wake you up, coupled with illumination. Lord Kitchener viewed a trial and ordered its general use, and many thousands were made under the supervision of the intrepid Staff Sergeant Bird. Perhaps he was the first Ammunition Technician; at least the use of Heath Robinson contraptions had arrived.

The First World War, 1914–1918

Another incident which was the result of a vivid imagination was during 1917 when Lieutenant George Finch, Royal Field Artillery, attached to the Army Ordnance Corps, was responsible for bringing down an enemy plane. Lieutenant Finch was transferred to the Corps doubtless due to his expert knowledge of chemistry. He was responsible for devising an efficient cure for the troublesome exudation in Amatol shell, and for this work received a grant from the 'Inventions' Committee. In Salonika a celebrated German pilot was particularly troublesome in shooting down observation balloons and the question was asked if it would be possible to fire a large explosive charge in a captive balloon that would be capable of destroying an enemy plane. The ingenious Lieutenant Finch arranged for some 500 to 600 pounds of explosives, primed with guncotton, to be placed in a 60-gallon container in the basket of a balloon, to be initiated by an electric charge. After extensive trials to eliminate the possibility of error, in November 1917 all was ready; the balloon, complete with bomb, was airborne. It was not until the 28 November that the lure attracted the first plane; about 150 yards above and slightly to one side when the bomb was fired. The wings closed upwards like leaves of a book, the tail broke and the successful career of the pilot Leutnant von Eschwege came to an abrupt end.

As a large part of this book deals with explosions of one sort or another and of the men who are so deeply involved, perhaps some reference to the actions from the 1914–1918 period is appropriate. What occurred then was the groundwork for the development of the Ammunition Service of today.

Quevilly – The build-up of the ammunition depots was beginning for the Somme offensive when there was an accidental explosion in the newly constructed depot at Quevilly in March 1916. This wrecked part of the depot and cost three lives. Lieutenant Reed, Army Ordnance Department, who was in charge of the unloading, was awarded the Military Cross for remaining at his post during continual explosions and for his efforts to quench the fires.

Audruicq – On the night of 20 July, Audruicq was blown up by one small well-placed bomb from a single enemy aircraft. 9,000 tons of ammunition were destroyed, loaded trucks acting as quick-match in carrying the fires from one shed to another. The destruction was stupendous – 'stacks of heavy shell detonated, boxed ammunition went up in a blaze of flaring cordite and exploding shell, and the major portion of the trench ammunition disappeared off the face of the earth.' Barographs several miles away recorded the violent air fluctuations, and live shells were recovered from a distance of two miles. The clearance of the debris, highly dangerous work, took several months, but was done without serious accident. The result of this incident was one crater oblong in shape, 60 feet deep, in which a battleship could have been docked, massive when you remember the size of the old warships that contained around 2,000 men.

Blargies – On the night of 19/20 May an organised attack by German aeroplanes under the command of the celebrated 'ace', von Richthofen, was made on Blargies. About 120 bombs were dropped on the depot itself, but little damage was done, as on this night the planes were well up in altitude. The same squadron returned the following night and was more successful; this was the only raid, except that at Audruicq in 1916, which put a depot temporarily out of action.

In his report Major Hopkins says that a shed full of 8-inch and 9.2-inch cartridges was immediately struck and its contents destroyed. Other bombs quickly took effect and soon the depot was blazing in five different directions. Low flying planes used their machine-guns to make it more difficult to cope with the incendiary fires. 'Work is proceeding today, the 22nd, on clearing the railway lines so that the remaining stocks may be available for issue as soon as possible. It is hoped that this work will be completed in two or three days' time. The railway lines are destroyed in numerous places, but traffic in the Main Depot was down as low as possible and no great amount of rolling stock was destroyed – at most fifty trucks and perhaps two locomotives. All loading orders had been completed and despatched except one train, half of which was saved by being run into an extension. All incoming traffic was also saved by removal to this area.'

5,000 tons of ammunition and a number of lives were lost, the casualties being mainly among those of the Army Ordnance Corps whose duty it was to fight fires. Three MCs, one DCM and two MMs were awarded to Army Ordnance Department Officers and Army Ordnance Corps WOs and NCOs for the part they played in combating this fire.

In another incident, on 10 March, when unloading the second train-load to enter the new depot, a box of 4.5-inch ammunition exploded; and, in spite of efforts to extinguish the flames, the fire spread, wrecked a considerable part of the depot and resulted in the loss of three lives. It was afterwards found out that ten rounds of this ammunition had been dropped when loading the ship at Newhaven, and the accident was probably due to a faulty No. 100 fuse, the first specially designed for the new high explosive shell, and one which led to trouble on several other occasions.

Not all incidents occurred overseas. The National Shell Filling Factory was located at Chilwell, Nottingham, during the First World War. During its period of production there were some nineteen accidental explosions, mostly of a minor nature. The most serious occurred at 7.10pm on 1 July 1918. The cause was, and still is, unknown. The devastation was considerable resulting in 134 dead and 340 injured; the event became known as the 'Great Explosion'. Houses and buildings over a wide area (Chilwell, Beeston, Attenborough and Toton) sustained structural damage. A study of the map of the area shows that this was a radius of approximately two miles from the centre of the explosion, massive by any measurement.

Despite the casualties only twelve of those people fit for work failed to report for duty the following day. The factory was soon rebuilt and back in full production, supplying high explosive shell for use on the Western Front for the final few months of the war.

During the early part of the war problems started coming to light with the various items of ammunition in use. It was recognised that it was unfair to blame the Ministry of Munitions or the manufacturers. Designers were being constantly called upon to produce some novelty at a moment's notice, for which there was no time for proper testing, and production was by then on an unprecedented scale with largely 'amateur' staff. The result of the various failures was that laboratory operations were in constant progress at each of the base depots. Also, work was always in hand to make minor repairs to ammunition which was then returned to the front lines.

It is recorded that in times of peace this sort of work was conducted solely by officers and NCO laboratory foremen (the first ammunition technical officers and Ammunition Technicians) who were trained as ammunition specialists. But due to the demand the supply of trained men quickly dried up. Ammunition schools were established in France at Zeneghem and Blargies. Instruction was both theoretical and practical and pupils were taught how to blow up blind shell. Some 432 officers passed through these schools, including men from Canada, Australia, New Zealand and the United States, beside far more numerous junior ranks. The idea for a permanent School of Ammunition had been created and would come to fruition in 1922 at Bramley. Ordnance officers were trained in ammunition at the School of Artillery, Woolwich.

The evolution of the specialised ammunition service continued during this period mainly brought about by the casual way others dealt with explosive stores. In 1917 ordnance ammunition units were created, one officer and eleven men, three units to each Army corps, increased to five units in 1918. Lectures were given by ordnance officers to explain the new types of ammunition and how to look after it to avoid damage. One result of these units being located near the front line was that prematures and other incidents could be much more clearly investigated, and defects in the ammunition noted for rectification in design and manufacture. Again a need for the future had been identified.

A Post-war Occupation (from *The Cologne Post*)

DISMANTLING SHELLS

Three hundred and fifty thousand tons of shells! When the war ended such was the amazing quantity of ammunition we had on our hands in France, where it was piled high on 3,500 acres. In a single heap there were 60,000 rounds of 6-inch shells, representing 2,300 tons of steel, about 20 tons of copper, and more than 240 tons of high explosives.

What was to be done with so vast an accumulation of 'superfluous' material? Was it to be fired aimlessly into the air or be cast into the sea, there to provide a nine days' wonder for the fishes? No. The lot was bought for £2,000,000, and ever since the work of converting it into material useful to our manufacturers has gone on steadily.

Every month about 2,000 tons of ammunition, as such, disappears, and in its place there are heaps of metal, chemicals, and so on, the components of such ammunition.

Great is the number of commodities recovered. In addition to steel, iron, brass, copper, lead, aluminium and many alloys, there are resin, numerous chemicals, gases, mechanical parts, rags, felt, cord etc. Every constituent except one is isolated and returned to this country for utilisation in the art of peace.

To obtain these results – in connection with which as many as 10,000 men and women have been engaged at one time – special methods are necessary. An unusual feature of the work is that cranes and other mechanical lifters are not employed. Every shell, after being raised by hand, is transported by means of gravity, and thus the risk of an explosion is minimised as much as possible.

If it is shrapnel, the case is first removed and the propellant extracted. Then, after the fuse and the bush have been taken from it, away it goes to a bench with a V-shaped top and a hopper underneath.

While it is resting here, nose downward, and at an angle of about 45 degrees, hammers play upon the exterior, loosening the contents – shrapnel and resin – which fall on a wire screen over the hopper. The resin rains through the screen, while the shrapnel rolls over it and drops into a box. Next, the copper band, having been cut through with a cold chisel, is wound off, and finally, the naked, harmless shell is stacked with hundreds of others in readiness for transport to England.

The Messines Mines, Belgium 1917

Warfare is at times rapid movement, at others a slow campaign blockading ports or laying siege to towns. The First World War was the last real war in which the opponents faced one another not far apart for long periods. Today one wonders at the tactics that were behind this sort of campaign. At Messines, over a two-year period, the Royal Engineers excavated some 21 deep and massive tunnels to lay mines which contained over 500 tons of high explosive. The idea was to set them off simultaneously and then to attack the devastated enemy lines. I do not intend to go into the difficulties of the engineers' task; it was extremely difficult. The main explosive used was ammonal, three times the power of gun-cotton and more stable to handle; it was packed in tins, each of the separate 21 mines containing varying amounts of explosive from 20,000lbs to over 95,000lbs in the largest. D-Day was 7 June. A German observer reported he saw 'eighteen' gigantic roses, with carmine petals like enormous mushrooms, which rose slowly and majestically out of the ground. The effects of this blast were felt in South East England. The problem was that only eighteen of the mines had exploded and due to the damage both above and below ground it proved difficult to resolve the problem of the remaining three monsters. One was 'traced ' and the 91,000lbs of ammonal were exploded. The crater left was some 430 feet in diameter. This crater was subsequently purchased by Lord Wakefield, as a war memorial, and renamed the 'Pool of Peace'.

The exact position of the remaining two mines remained a mystery until 17 July 1955 when, during a severe thunderstorm, there was a mighty and unexpected explosion. Fortunately no one was even injured. The other still remains and one can only wonder how and when, if ever, some act in the future will create the last of the 21 craters. Battlefield clearance is taken far more seriously today.

Research has revealed many interesting items, some still covered by security classification. However, there have been a number that can be included and the following perhaps gives an interesting insight into the immediate pre-war period of 1939 at a time when many people realised what was about to happen.

CHAPTER 3

EXPLOSIVE ORDNANCE DISPOSAL TRAINING AND INFORMATION

The Army School of Ammunition* was established in 1922 at the Central Ammunition Depot, Bramley, from a small detachment from the training establishment at Hilsea, Portsmouth. The original purpose of the school was to train civilian ammunition examiners. The early days of the control of the quality of ammunition was very much a civilian matter, left in the hands of the manufacturers and in those days of high quality there was not a lot that could really go wrong.

The first course for Inspectors of Ordnance Machinery held at Bramley, to train officers fully in the technical aspects of ammunition, was held in April 1924. For no apparent reason prior to this momentous date little training had been given to officers on ammunition. Their technical expertise on the weapons was first class and this additional training was intended to ensure that in the future a simple inspection would be able to determine the cause of any failure, be it in the weapon or the ammunition.

Perhaps it is appropriate at this stage to explain entry into the Royal Army Ordnance Corps for officers. Prior to 1939 it was not possible to be directly commissioned into the Corps. Only those engineer-trained personnel, Ordnance Mechanical Engineers and those promoted to hold Quartermaster's Commissions obtained direct entry; all others were transferred from other units within the Army. The main requirement was that they had served for a minimum of three years in their own regiment, had passed the promotion examination to Captain and subsequently passed the Ordnance Officer's Course.

There were a variety of reasons why men left their old regiments and joined the Corps. Money was one. In the period between the two wars for example, on transfer, regimental pay increased dramatically from thirteen shillings a day to 23 shillings. Another valid reason was to enhance

* From 1922 to 1953 the School was known as 'B' Branch, the Training Establishment. In 1953 it became the 'The School of Ammunition RAOC'. The establishment was located at the Central Ammunition Depot Bramley. In 1974 when larger premises were required the school moved to its present site at the Central Ammunition Depot, Kineton.

promotion prospects. A long-retired former member of the Corps recalls that in 1936 the Royal Warwickshire Regiment had subalterns who wore the 1914–18 war medals. It is hard to imagine today a lieutenant serving in the rank for eighteen years! No wonder there was a fair amount of competition. Captain (later Major General) John Sheffield, the athlete who competed in the 1936 Olympic Games, suffered from polio and had to transfer on medical grounds. In this case the infantry's loss was obviously the Corps' gain. My contributor recalls one other who transferred, along with a brother officer's wife.

The prewar Ordnance Officer's course was very similar to that of the AE; it was of approximately one year's duration, split into three parts. The longest was at the Military College of Science, Woolwich. This covered science subjects, chemistry of explosives and the design of ammunition. Part was at the school at Bramley: practical work in proof testing and storage of ammunition and explosives, demolition and repair work. Finally the non-ammunition training part of the course was at Hilsea. One contributor recalls that during his training there were two Egyptian officers there, one of whom had to be restrained from dealing with an instantaneous fuse with a hammer.

The course was held in 1939 and my contributor clearly remembers Major Temple Morris advising trainees that Hitler had invaded Poland, and that his

Army School of Ammunition

Chief Instructors

1922/23	Major W. N. Stokes
1924/25	Major A. R. Valon
1925/28	Major W. H. Verschoyle-Campbell
1928/31	Major C. T. F. Haigh
1931/35	Major A. W. A. Harker
1935/38	Major T. Morris
1938/40	Major R. G. L. Ford
1940/42	Major R. M. N. Patrick
1942/43	Major A. W. Field
1943/44	Major E. M. Ketley
1944/45	Major R. Sylvester
1945/46	Major H. Phillips
1946/49	Major A. Cripps
1949/51	Major B. W. Thompson
1951/53	Major W. Froggett
1953/56	Lieutenant Colonel Col R. V. Peters
1956/59	Lieutenant Colonel R. L. Allen
1959/62	Lieutenant Colonel C. W. Douch
1962/65	Lieutenant Colonel G. R. Bathe
1965/69	Lieutenant Colonel J. H. Lawrence-Archer
1969/71	Lieutenant Colonel G. H. Hale
1971/74	Lieutenant Colonel M. Haywood
1974/77	Lieutenant Colonel J. E. Hart
1977	Lieutenant Colonel J. D. Grant
1977/79	Lieutenant Colonel L. Guy

Commanding Officers

1979/81	Lieutenant Colonel L. Guy
1981/83	Lieutenant Colonel C. M. G. Hendy OBE
1983/85	Lieutenant Colonel H. G. Heap
1985/87	Lieutenant Colonel S. G. de Wolfe
1987/89	Lieutenant Colonel D. W. Townsend
1993/96	Lieutenant Colonel S. J. Crowe MBE
1996–	Lieutenant Colonel D. B. Doherty

immediate posting was to be Staff Captain Ammunition to GHQ, BEF France. He recalls that the headquarters staff was a motley crew, several brigadiers, various colonels, a host of junior ranks with warrant officers, sergeants and rank and file, mostly reservists, just called up with no idea what they were all supposed to do. He also remembers that whilst taking an erratic train journey across France with the headquarters staff, two cooks were sent off to make a brew of tea. Typical of the cookhouse staff, the train left without them; two weeks later they turned up without the tea but having taken a short trip to Marseilles.

At the end of 1941 this contributor took over command of the school. The changes from 1939 were obvious, major expansion to deal with officers and men, far shorter and more concentrated courses, a wider range of ammunition and a change in the students, many if not most of whom had some sort of background of basic scientific knowledge. The life in the war years was very hectic and the working practices of the commanding officer were compared to that of a headmaster and not really the commander of an army unit. Perhaps this view was strengthened by the fact that his two senior instructors, Captains Field and Manfield, had both been schoolmasters prior to joining the Army. He clearly recalls the considerable help from the civilian staff, a Mr Lee who looked like Neville Chamberlain but whose knowledge of ammunition of all types was encyclopedic; and a Mr Love, a highly skilled craftsman, an expert in dismantling and cutting into display sections, ammunition and fuses. Regrettably one day a detonator exploded, causing injury and the loss of a finger. Despite the loss Mr Love served at the school for many years.

The forerunner of the Ammunition Examiner was the Military Laboratory Foreman and in 1923 the importance of this work was recognised and the trade was accepted by the Army, classified as an 'A' trade and the name changed. The early courses lasted for a full year and were held at somewhat irregular intervals. In those early days a requirement for the course was an Army Certificate of Education Class 2. With this anyone in the right place at the right time who applied for training would be accepted. The training staff at the school was then very small, a major as chief instructor, a senior NCO and a couple of civilian instructors, with a few soldiers and civilians for administrative purposes.

One of the eminent members of the trade, who trained in 1938, recalls that his course started off with about 30 students, all with the required second class Army Certificate of Education. The course lasted about a year and commenced with two months at Bramley on elementary chemistry. By examination failure the numbers reduced to about fourteen, who then proceeded to the Military College of Science, Cambridge Barracks, Frances Street, Woolwich, for approximately six months. At Woolwich the students studied chemistry and explosive chemistry. They actually manufactured small quantities of explosives and then had the thrill of testing them to see if they worked. Time was also spent at Woolwich Arsenal, with training in the entire manufacturing process, including cartridge cases, and at that time aircraft bombs. They then returned to Bramley for the final months for more practical training, breaking down fuses, heat testing of cordite and the usual demolition training.

An unusual feature at this time was that AEs were also responsible for respirators (gas masks). Two weeks were spent on actually making them, as well as on repair work. There were no course papers issued pre-wa; a student had to listen and write up his notes as he went along, including all drawings and diagrams necessary to record how every fuse functioned.

The examinations were set by the instructors and were not easy. There was no choice. For example, there were eight questions on chemistry and explosives and another eight, again without choice, on ammunition. For the practical exam, each student selected from a choice, a sealed envelope in which were three 'jobs' to do.

The three tests of 1938 are still well remembered. The first was on the 45 fuse used with the six-inch coastal defence ammunition, for which he had to remove all safety devices apart from the impact device, then retire to the proof block and fire the fuse. The second task was similar but on the 119 fuse and gaine. Finally he had a heat test of cordite. None of the tasks were unduly complicated or difficult but with the examiner at his elbow to ensure every task was performed in the right sequence, the fear of failure and therefore another year at Bramley, the average student was a bag of nerves; hence the clear recollection of the ordeal of over fifty years ago.

Marks on the course were also given for the note books and diagrams that had been prepared over the year. There was no system of averaging marks over the final exams, and in order to qualify as a Class 1 student you had to obtain 85 per cent or more in all three tests. Class 2 was 75–84 per cent and Class 3 65–74 per cent. (On the 1938 course were two students on their third attempt.)

Once qualified and with a second class certificate of education and a second class trade qualification, a soldier could then sit for the lance corporal's examination. Promotion to sergeant required a first class education certificate, first class trade and a vacancy. At that time there were only about 50 Ammunition Examiners on the total establishment.

For promotion to the ultimate rank of warrant officer class one, a warrant officer class two had to go back to school. All WO1s were clerks, hence the need to start again. Obviously clerks were more highly thought of than AEs.

The commencement of hostilities in 1939 caused a panic all round, including in the ammunition world. The basic experience of 1914–18 was that technical personnel were required not far from the front line. This meant there was an immediate need for a considerable increase in numbers as there were only about 50 AEs in the Army at that time. The training course was immediately reduced from one year to three months, the size of each intake was increased and the number of courses also increased to about twelve a year. As will be appreciated promotion prospects for the existing 50 AEs was excellent. The dawning of a new age had arrived.

Now the course was very condensed but it broadly followed the same pattern. The atmosphere of the school could perhaps be compared to a modern sixth form science college. A little known fact is that during the 1939–1945 period another strange phenomenon appeared, an Assistant Ammunition Examiner (ATS). For those who do not recognise the letters this meant a 'qualified woman'. Many old soldiers will find that hard to believe, but it is true and can be verified from WRAC Records and photographs.

These Assistant AEs were employed at the Central Ammunition Depots in the United Kingdom; their task was mainly the inspection and reconditioning of ammunition, damaged or spoilt by flooding in the holds of ships, or by other adverse treatment. They reconditioned otherwise unusable ammunition at a time in our history when every single item was desperately needed. They worked under the orders and control of a very young ATS officer, perhaps the only Ammunition Officer of this sex in history whose name I have not been able to trace. She would be in her 70s if still alive today.

Their training consisted of a six week course, held at a Central Ammunition Depot. Training was similar to that of the men at the time, which lasted twelve weeks. It covered theory and practical in classification, recognition, composition, construction and functions for all types of UK land service ammunition, including emphasis on working practices and safety precautions, regulations in laboratories, magazines and repair factories.

Although in the ATS the trade was only classified as Group B, Class 1 and 2, their duties were very similar to those of their male colleagues. The Assistant Ammunition Examiner was generally a lance corporal on passing out, and could expect promotion to corporal and sergeant. Again, not dissimilar to her male counterpart, the basic requirements were for a person who was practical, who enjoyed manual work, was able to organise and supervise others and was obviously required to be at ease working with explosives. A degree of strength was also indicated as a requirement in the ATS job analyses of 1946.

One of these ladies, Barbara Green, trained at Bramley and was posted to CAD Corsham in 1946 as a corporal. She was then posted to CAD Kineton and promoted to sergeant. Whilst at Kineton she met her husband to be who was then chief clerk. Major W. J. Clarke and his AE wife Barbara served a total of 34 years in the Corps.

In addition to the ATS holding the qualification of Assistant Ammunition Examiners, after the war and during the early days of national service (when the engagement was limited to eighteen months) a small number of men undertook a short course at Bramley and passed out as Assistant AEs. Little is now known of this era but it would appear that the Assistant AE was in fact one grade below the fully qualified operator. An Assistant trade Class 2 would be equivalent to a fully qualified AE Class 3. However this grading lasted about as long as the eighteen month period of national service.

The Army Apprentices' College at Chepstow also played a very valuable part in catching the potential AE and later AT at a young age. The training of these apprentices for the trade started in 1955 and continued until 1992 when the college closed. Originally known as the Ammunition Examiners' Department, the first six trainees were under the watchful eyes of Captain J. Harrison and Staff Sergeant R. T. Dallen RAOC. In the years that followed to 1981 some 300 apprentices had received training in the technical side of the job prior to attending the adult course at the School of Ammunition. In later years the ammunition technical staff was increased: a captain, a WO1, two staff sergeants and a civilian instructor supported by a senior storeman and a labourer. The training these young men received fitted them well in the traditions of the service; many have received awards for gallantry and eight have given their lives in the service of their country following their chosen profession.

From the early 1950s the intake of potential AEs included a very high proportion of national servicemen. For many reasons these young men were different from the regular recruit, their main asset being their educational background. Many actually had degrees, and all had at least the school certificate that required a pass level in at least six subjects of which one had to be mathematics and one was usually science based. As recruits, potential officers were segregated for basic training and within this group were all the potential AEs. Although some very strange academic types were selected and trained the majority were more normal beings.

There were various training activities undertaken outside the training school such as the trip to visit the Royal Ordnance factories at Blackburn and Chorley. The highlight of this trip was the evening out in Bury being 'lodged' at the dreadful 'Victorian' depot of the Lancashire Fusiliers.

Another trip during the course was to the depot at Buckingham to gain some 'hands-on' experience. For the writer of this book, part of this period was in a repair factory with a qualified corporal and what seemed like at least 100 rather basic ladies who were highly successful in embarrassing one so young, whilst testing 3.7-inch anti-aircraft shells by inserting them into a large cylindrical gauge. Another of the tasks was to ensure the paint work on the shell was satisfactory. Readers from the trade will know the routine but for others each shell was painted a basic colour, for example, yellow or buff to indicate high explosive, black for armour piercing, with coloured bands to indicate type of explosive filling and various other symbols for the type of smoke indicator. Comments were often made by some of these ladies that indicated their intention to try and carry out a specialist repainting job on certain parts of the anatomy if one did not behave. Their possible treatment of any AEs who intended matrimony does not bear thinking about.

After their basic training at what seemed a godforsaken spot called Blackdown Camp, recruits went off to CAD Bramley to the Ammunition School. Technical training was a dramatic change after the first months. There was little 'bullshit', not much drill and a much more casual life and, although life in barracks in the '50s was spartan, it was a start with certain promotion to corporal.

The training at the school in the 1950s was basically the same as it had been for over a decade and it would continue in broadly the same way for a further twenty years. There was daily tuition in the classroom, pages and pages of foolscap printed study notes, to read and learn and frequent examinations. Failure could mean a life as a cook or even worse general duties. Pay in those days was very poor for the national servicemen, 21/- (£1.05p) per week; but, although better for the regular soldier, 49/- (£2.45p) it was still basic and so outside activities did not interfere with constant study.

One great incentive to do well was that on passing out successfully the person with the highest overall marks on a course had the choice of all the postings. For a national servicemen this was worth the effort. With luck there could be a posting to a depot near his home. The number of home postings was vast in those early days; from Carlisle to Corsham for the large ammunition depots, several smaller locations such as Buckingham, down to the various commands and mobile units. There was little competition for overseas postings in those days.

To qualify as an Ammunition Examiner Class 2 a student had to achieve an average over 75 per cent; Class 3 about 65 per cent. Class 1 was not available without further practical experience.

Although the majority of students were national servicemen there were a number of regulars and some anomalies such as one 'senior' who proudly wore Royal Air Force pilot's wings as a lance corporal. He had left the Royal Air Force after the war and, unable to settle down or rejoin, he became an Ammunition Examiner. He was one of the few with decorations for bravery in the air. Another young man served in the Merchant Navy as a boy. He was called up for national service some years later complete with his war medals and the Atlantic Star. One of the instructors at the school in the period of national service can remember facing a class of 23 students to teach them basic explosive chemistry and on enquiry discovered that seven of them had degrees in chemistry.

At this time if you passed the course and qualified as an Ammunition Examiner Class 2 you gained the automatic rank of corporal. Some months later a further examination could be taken at your own depot for upgrade to Class 1, which brought automatic promotion to sergeant.

Prior to 1954 the highest trade rating in the army was six stars. Each star obtained brought more money, some earned an extra 3/6 per week (17p), some 7/– (35p), not a fortune but stars and rank made life a little more comfortable. In 1954 the X trade rating was introduced. Class 1 AEs were now X1 Tradesmen. No one really knew or cared whether it was for technical ability or danger pay.

AMENDMENTS TO SENIORITY ROLL
CORPS ORDER NO. 45

AMMUNITION EXAMINERS ROLL

Promoted Sergeant w.e.f. dates as shown:–

NEXT AFTER 22787923 BROWN, W. (8)
22540292 L/Cpl Bruce, D. 22.10.53 1st A.E.I 15.07.17

NEXT AFTER 22658827 BAINBRIDGE, G. (8)
22661401 Cpl Thomas, J. R. 03.11.53 Ex. A.E.I 29.05.30
22787241 Cpl Featherstone, 03.11.53 Ex. A.E.I 03.10.33

P.D.
22680118 Cpl Baxter, R. C. W. 03.11.53 Ex. A.E.I 09.05.29
22674100 Cpl Page, J. W. 03.11.53 Ex. A.E.I 20.03.34
22668794 Cpl Maidment, K. 03.11.53 Ex. A.E.I 06.01.34

NEXT AFTER 22805388 EDWARD, A. D. (8)
22807907 Cpl Holden, G. A. 28.11.53 Ex. A.E.I 18.10.34

NEXT AFTER 22807394 ANDERSON, J. (8)
22697524 Cpl Southwart, D. 31.12.53 Ex. A.E.I 06.02.33

NEXT AFTER 22648992 DAVISON, P. M. (8)
22723799 Cpl Harding, G. 05.02.54 Ex. A.E.I 30.03.33
22723460 Cpl Harrison, R. 05.02.54 Ex. A.E.I 15.05.30
22717816 Cpl Holt, A. 05.02.54 Ex. A.E.I 09.09.30
22723463 Cpl Robinson, G. 05.02.54 Ex. A.E.I 14.04.29
22650498 Cpl Dando, J. 09.02.54 Ex. A.E.I 10.11.32
22726348 Cpl Scriven, A. 09.02.54 Ex. A.E.I 29.06.30
22726293 Cpl Parnell, E. 18.02.54 Ex. A.E.I 19.08.34
22711174 Cpl Baldwin, G. 18.02.54 Ex. A.E.I 14.03.34
22724286 Cpl Dewhirst, T. 18.02.54 Ex. A.E.I 25.03.34
22720757 Cpl Sclater, J. 18.02.54 Ex. A.E.I 03.02.31
22726337 Cpl Bannister, D. 18.02.54 Ex. A.E.I 23.07.30
22725002 Cpl Humpage, B. 18.02.54 Ex. A.E.I 20.02.33
22621081 L/Cpl Frankland, E. 04.03.54 Ex. A.E.I 29.06.32
22733848 Cpl Hyland, J. 10.03.54 Ex. A.E.I 12.04.33
22726294 Cpl Place, R. 10.03.54 Ex. A.E.I 15.04.31
22729151 Cpl Bailey, J. 15.03.54 Ex. A.E.I 26.09.33
22731611 Cpl Glover, A. 15.03.54 Ex. A.E.I 01.11.30

A soldier could follow his progress on the seniority roll by the regular amendments published in the *Corps Gazette.* In the example shown, the first date is that when the first class trade qualification was obtained, followed by the Army Certificate of Education held (note that most on the list were exempt), finally the date of birth.

In 1952 there was a requirement that every soldier was capable of engaging the enemy in times of need. He was supposedly a soldier first and a tradesman second. For this reason a requirement was introduced for a further course to be passed for qualifying for staff sergeant. This included military subjects such as map-reading, drill and military law.

During the post-war period training was somewhat chaotic. A former commanding officer of the school, Howard Cripps, recalls that he attended the first post-war Inspecting Ordnance Officer (IOOs) course from January 1946 – February 1947. In those heady days the ammunitions section of the Military College of Science was located in 'dreary dismal' premises at Stoke-on-Trent, the students' accommodation being if at all possible, even worse. Immediately after completing the course Howard Cripps was posted to Bramley as Chief Instructor, together with two other members who joined as instructors. Of these three officers only one, and not Howard Cripps, had ever practised what they then set about preaching. This strange anomaly was really caused by the dramatic demobilisation of the wartime soldier and the emergence of national service to fill the gap. This was a time when there was much wartime ammunition lying around all over the United Kingdom, and overseas, waiting to be cleared.

During the period 1947–1950 there were never less than eight AE courses running at the school at any one time. The numbers on each course varied between 15–20 students at that time due to a shortage of instructors. It was therefore not unusual for the best on a course to join the instruction staff as soon as they qualified. Not only did they have no practical experience in the field, but they had received no training in how to teach others. It was really only the prior ability of these young national servicemen that enabled the entire programme to continue in a reasonable way.

Training at Bramley continued in the same basic fashion until late 1953. It is generally recognised that the period 1945–1953 was one of total lack of forward planning, missed opportunities with little or no clearly defined objectives. Recruitment of regular soldiers as AEs had been negligible. On the writer's own course, only two out of 30 were regulars, the rest could only work in the trade for the balance of their national service, probably a year at most. Also around this time there were far too many AEs on the establishment of ammunition units; many really wasted their skills in work well below their training capability, bearing in mind that most students were BSc material and many actually held degrees.

1953 saw a major administrative change, 'B' Branch became officially 'The School of Ammunition, RAOC'. From being formally the chief instructor, a major, the senior officer now officially became a commanding officer with the rank of lieutenant colonel. The school then came under the direct control of the Commander Ammunition Organisation who gave clear directions, selected staff of the right calibre and who, more importantly, provided full support. From this strong influence the school went from strength to strength and very close working ties were created with the Royal Military College of Science.

This period was one in direct contrast with earlier times with the opportunity taken for development. The present school is accepted as the best in the world, its students are highly trained to deal with the complexities of the range and constantly changing types of modern ammunition. The training in dealing with improvised explosive devices was easily and rapidly taken on board as needs arose, from the early days of Cyprus, Aden and Hong Kong to those terrible days from the late 1960s when the present IRA campaign started in Northern Ireland. The development of the school was complemented by the changing profile of the ideal Ammunition Technical Officer and Ammunition Technician. A further development in status occurred in 1968 when it became 'The Army School of Ammunition'.

Because of the increasing complexity of ammunition loadings and the equipment in use, including the development of guided missile systems, the school outgrew the old site at Bramley and moved to its present location at CAD Kineton in 1974.

In approximately 1970, the Army decided to take a closer look at the training of all technicians. In the case of AEs, now classified as ATs, this really was a welcome improvement. As certain ammunition tasks could only be undertaken by Class 1 tradesmen this work was excluded from the training schedule until the upgrading training. The time lapse between leaving the school and taking the upgrading course to Class 1 was no longer to be a matter of months but years; and without a more formal training programme it was becoming very difficult to obtain.

The ammunition school formed a team to look at the work undertaken by ATs worldwide and to find out what they were required to do. Visiting and interviewing those on the job revealed that much could be done to improve their training.

The basic course was altered and students were then trained to do those tasks that their trade class and rank allowed. Later when they had obtained practical experience they returned to the school for a further three months for upgrading to Class 1.

The basic course of approximately six months included six weeks at the Royal Military College of Science at Shrivenham from 1983 onwards covering basic chemistry and physics relating to explosives. This improvement was introduced due to the lack of resources within the Royal Army Education Corps to provide training at the School of Ammunition.

Since 1980 all successful students qualify as Class 2 tradesmen and since 1982/83 all pass out as lance corporals. After a year's probation they are then promoted to corporal. The logic behind this change was that a lance corporal could easily be downgraded, whilst this was much more difficult for a corporal. After about three years the AT returned to the school for the three-month training course and was then upgraded to Class 1.

As with all carefully thought out plans some deficiencies appeared. In 1983 there was a severe shortage of senior NCOs, so the time as a Class 2 tradesman was reduced to two years and the course was increased to four months. To give the reader an idea of the numbers involved, in 1985 there were two upgrading courses each year, increased to three in 1988; on each course there was a maximum number of sixteen students.

In addition to the ATs' courses the School of Ammunition is also responsible for training Ammunition Technical Officers (ATOs). Their course is far longer and more comprehensive and is split with approximately six months at Shrivenham and seven months at the school. The students are not only from the British Army but include many from overseas. The 1967 ATO course consisted of eighteen students; twelve British, two Canadians, two Singaporeans and two Malays. There is now only one course each year with a maximum of twenty students.

Regular joint services special anti-terrorist courses are run, of three weeks' duration, along with the advanced improvised explosive device disposal courses.

There is a great shortage of archival material about the School of Ammunition, not only for the pre-war period but even in more recent years, but available is a list of all those who qualified at Bramley and Kineton from September 1939 Course 1 to September 1961 Course 271, some 6,000 young men in 22 years. Some examples of the courses, dates and numbers who were successful :

Course 111 Qualified December 1946 14 Students

Course 129 Qualified July 1948 27 Students

Course 193 Qualified July 1952 28 Students

Course 254 Qualified August 1958 17 Students

Course 268 Qualified September 1960 12 Students

This was the last course for Ammunition Examiners. Course 269 qualifying in February 1961 produced the first 12 Ammunition Technicians.

The results of three of the courses selected at random (apart from 193 which was the author's own) are shown on this and the following pages.

From its beginnings in 1922 with a complement of one officer, effectively a 'jack of all trades', the school now has a permanent staff of nine officers and a considerable permanent staff of both military and civilian personnel. The figures of those involved in the trade over the years give some idea of the required output of the school:-

1895 2 Laboratory Foremen. Senior NCOs.

1913 46 Laboratory Foremen all ranks, also classed as Clerks.

1922 35 all ranks, still classed as dual role tradesmen.

1930 52 Ammunition Examiners below the rank of WO1.

1937 48 Ammunition Examiners.

1990 325 Ammunition Technicians on the RAOC establishment.

RAOC Training Centre Ammunition Wing, 18 December 1946
Results of the 11th Ammunition Examiners' Course, 14 August to 16 December 1946

Order of Merit	Number	Rank	Name	Regiment	%	Classification
1	7650474	Cpl	Penwarden, K.	RAOC	91	D
2	14083562	Pte	Austin, W.	"	84	D
3	14041342	"	Duncan, A.	SWB	82	D
4	7601445	"	Dell, A. W.	RAOC	77	Q1
5	14165788	"	Medico, I. V.	"	72	Q1
5	14137979	"	Oakes, N. J.	"	72	Q1
7	14140667	"	Brown, J. S.	"	70	Q1
8	14186584	"	Harrolds, J.	"	69	Q2
9	14147513	"	Hawtree, M.	"	67	Q2
10	14129641	"	Ford, R.	"	66	Q2
11	14112470	"	Brown, J.	"	65	Q2
11	14185985	"	Burgess, K. L.	"	65	Q2
13	14140305	"	Glover, E.	"	64	F
14	14145938	"	McIntosh, J.	"	60	F

Summary: 12 passes and 2 fails.

RESULTS OF THE 193 AMMUNITION EXAMINERS COURSE which terminated on 23rd July 1952:

				QUALIFICATION
1	22587403	L/Cpl	Starkey, R. J.	AEII
2	22590352	"	Swann, B.	AEII
3	22598428	"	Wright, A.	AEII
4	22589157	"	Evans, R. D.	AEII
5	22583581	"	Wade, K.	AEII
6	22598426	"	Dinaldson, I. J.	AEII
7	22594713	"	Holliman, A. C.	AEII
8	22597513	"	Bazzard, C. L. B.	AEII
9	22596344	"	Blakemore, T.	AEII
10	22563335	"	Greenwood, D. N.	AEII
11	22577895	"	Leitch, J. D.	AEII
12	22597267	"	Newman, R. V.	AEII
13	22597790	"	Fosh, J. B.	AEII
14	22596956	"	Duncan, R.	AEII
15	22771701	"	Birchall, P.	AEII
16	22584809	"	Beadle, P. R.	AEII
17	22584811	"	Kennedy, I. P.	AEII
18	22585522	"	Sloan, H.	AEII
19	22588859	"	Durham, D. S.	AEII
20	22582580	"	Norton, D. K.	AEII
21	22594690	"	Willis, M.	AEII
22	22292656	"	Anderson, G. E.	AEII
23	22598427	"	Porter, D.	AEIII
24	22597266	"	Folkes, L. J.	AEIII
25	22584810	"	Bevan, B.	AEIII
26	22772013	"	Clifford, A.	AEIII
27	22583629	"	Lloyd, T. F.	AEIII
28	22587516	"	McAllister, A	FAIL

Summary 27 passes, 1 fail (back squaded to Course 194). 22 AEII, 5 AEIII

RESULT OF THE 268 EXAMINERS COURSE which terminated on 28th September 1960

				QUALIFICATION
1	23649708	Cpl	Spencer, H. J.	AEII
2	23644109	"	Daykin, A.	AEII
3	23753117	"	Payne, G.	AEII
4	23644443	"	Cotton, B. R.	AEII
5	23645329	"	Ratnett, H. G.	AEII
6	23644352	"	Nobbs, L. J.	AEII
7	23466132	"	Gray, L. J.	AEII
8	23734712	"	Squires, W. C.	AEII
9	23607731	"	Littler, G.	AEII
10	23354142	"	Burton, F.	AEII
11	23649873	Pte	Cooper, W. E.	Stm/Ammo
12	23735435	Pte	Ryder, M. F. J.	Stm/Ammo

Summary 10 passes, 2 fail, (failures classified as ammunition storemen Grade BIII)

During the 1939 to 1945 war period the numbers increased very dramatically. Some 300 men each year were trained and this level continued through national service.

The School is now truly international; students from some 96 different countries have attended courses and some 1,300 students a year pass through the school. The range of courses is now considerable, no longer limited to the single requirement of training officers and men as Ammunition Technical Officers and Ammunition Technicians. Specialist training is available to the Royal Air Force, the Royal Navy and to civilians.

It is a sad fact that the British Army is probably the most experienced force in the world in dealing with terrorist devices, not only from two decades in Northern Ireland, but from Cyprus, Aden, Hong Kong and many other places. This experience is now highly valued by other nations.

The Army School of Ammunition organises a considerable number of specialist training courses every year; those which apply specifically to EOD duties include the following:

Pre-selection: a two-week course for those who have passed the initial basic tests. This course selects the candidates from all services for training as AT Class 2.

Ammunition Technician: Class 2, this is the main training for the trade, the course lasts for approximately eight months. On successful completion, the trainee is posted to a base unit in the UK or Germany for at least six months, in the rank of lance corporal for this probationary period.

Ammunition Technician: Class 1, after at least two years' service in the trade Class 2 ATs undergo the upgrading course which lasts approximately two months. On satisfactory completion they are then fully trained, but are still not qualified to deal with Improvised Explosive Devices.

Basic Operators: EOD, a pre-selection board nominates officers and soldiers for this basic course to qualify personnel for the intermediate training; this course is of approximately two weeks' duration.

Intermediate EOD (IEDD): Ammunition Technicians Class 1 are now trained as IEDD operators for general war service and to prepare them for the advanced training; the course lasts two weeks.

Advanced Operational EOD (IEDD): Ammunition Technicians of the rank of sergeant or above; Class 1 tradesmen who have successfully completed the Intermediate EOD course now undertake further specialist training to qualify and be licensed to conduct IEDD Operations not only on the UK mainland but world-wide, excluding Northern Ireland. The course lasts for three weeks. This is the training course that is extended to eligible EOD personnel from the Royal Navy, RAF and Royal Engineers.

Operational EOD (IEDD) Northern Ireland, No. 2s: This is a three-week course for Ammunition Technicians Class 1 sergeants and above, to further train and licence them for operational duties as team No. 2s in Northern Ireland.

Operational EOD (IEDD): Operation Northern Ireland; this is a three-week course for Ammunition Technicians Class 1 again sergeants and above. This specialist training involves the detailed operational procedures necessary before personnel undertake a tour of duty in Northern Ireland.

It is not necessary for a soldier or officer to attend all these courses; for example provided the advanced operational course has been attended, some personnel then miss out the No. 2 training. To perform in safety is the prime factor; although adequate training to ensure an operator has received all the required skills is paramount, some are exceptional men and aspects of training do not need any duplication.

There is a further course that covers a degree of training now considered necessary for those who are selected for promotion from staff sergeant to WO2. This is a one-week course that instructs these highly skilled professionals in the duties of WO2s.

The following was what was expected of them in 1925.

THE ROYAL ARMY ORDNANCE CORPS GAZETTE, NOVEMBER 1925

Half-yearly Qualifying Examination for Promotion.

The following general rules and instructions should be carefully noted, as, to save space, they will not be given in further republications. Where, however, the details of time allowed, maximum marks obtainable and qualifying minimum, etc. differ in any particular paper from those laid down below, they will be shown. – Ed.

Time allowed - three hours. Total marks allotted are in parentheses at end of each question; maximum obtainable, 120; qualifying minimum 78 = 65%.

Before commencing your answers read the above instructions and each question carefully.

Show your trade and index number and nothing else plainly on the front of your Army Book 4. No reference to number, rank or name is to be made.

* * *

Staff Sergeants to Quartermaster Sergeants, Ammunition Examiners, Clerks and Storemen.

In accordance with paragraph 55 R.A.O.C. S.O.-4th May 1925.

N.B. – Questions 1–4 should be answered by all candidates, 5 and 6 by Clerks only, 7 and 8 by Storemen only, and ammunition examiners may answer any two from 5 to 8 inclusive.

1. A certain unit from Aldershot was encamped on Salisbury Plain; they received their equipment from O.O. Tidworth and when handing it in to that officer on termination of the camp a number of deficiencies were brought to light. Give in detail the procedure followed to recover the value of the stores, showing to whom the money is paid and explaining how the Auditor at the issuing depot will know that the money has been paid (20).

2. Where do R.A.O.C. Reservists residing in Great Britain rejoin the colours if mobilisation is ordered?

What officer is responsible for:– (a) calling them up? (b) Equipping and clothing them?

How are reservist's kits stored and how is turnover arranged?

Give a brief description of a War Equipment Table and state for what purpose these are used.

How are 'mobilisation' barrels for machine guns marked and what are the orders with regard to these barrels? (20)

3. An indent is received in a certain group for stores which are not available; describe in detail the whole of the action which should be taken by the storeholder concerned in accordance with the procedure laid down by R.A.O.S. Part 1. Particulars of all the heads under which information would be given by the storeholder on any report he made, and of any records and documents he would mark up, are required. (20)

4. Describe fully the procedure which is laid down to be followed when purchasing stores of one kind the purchase price of which exceeds £50. Local purchase has been approved by A.D.O.S.P. and the station concerned is situated at home. (20)

5. A quantity of 'materials for repair' is issued to an infantry battalion – (a) How does the unit account for these? (b) What are the steps which should be taken in the command to see that the above stores have been properly expended? (20)

6. You are chief clerk to the A.D.O.C. Aldershot Command. The Colonel Commandant of an Infantry Brigade has submitted through Divisional H.Q. to H.Q. Aldershot Command that the scale of 'Guns, Lewis, DP.' should be increased from 2 to 6 per battalion; he has pointed out that companies are trained independently, as is also the A.A. Section of the Headquarter Wing. Further he insists that plenty of instructions in stripping is essential, and that the Batt. Commanders have had to authorise the stripping of service guns in order to give this instruction. Your A.D.O.S. agrees that the increase is most desirable.

Prepare a letter to the War Office stating the case as strongly as possible and prepared for signature by the correct authority. (20)

7. (i) The Oil and Paint Store is in your group. State what precautions you would take: (a) against fire; (b) to keep your stocks in good condition; (c) to avoid harm coming to anybody employed in the group.

(ii) A consignment of oil has been received from overseas, several drums have leaked on the way and 4 gallons of oil, value nineteen shillings, are deficient. What action would you take when dealing with the documents connected with the receipt of the stores?

N.B.– There is nothing to show that the consignment has been badly handled in transit. (20)

8. You are in charge of camp equipment at a depot and there are a number of small repairs to tentage, etc., which have to be carried out in the group after the camping season. Give in detail the procedure laid down in R.A.O.S. Part I for – (a) drawing and expending the necessary materials; (b) adjusting the account after the stores have been repaired.

How is the transaction costed and how does the Local Auditor know that the materials shown in the voucher have been used for a particular service? (20)

In any year the school is now an extremely busy college. Around 60 specialist training courses are organised, lasting from one week to eight months for soldiers, and over a year for the Ammunition Technical Officers. Students come from all services within the British war machine, from our NATO allies and from countries within the Commonwealth and other allied nations. The only restrictions are that they are allies and have a good command of technical English.

Terrorism is regrettably a growth industry and of all nations perhaps the British are now the most experienced in anti-terrorist training, and have the most practical and sophisticated equipment. This knowledge is of great value and provided an applicant nation is friendly and acceptable then this specialised knowledge is willingly passed on to their technical personnel.

The school is still the sole organisation that trains the technician for Improvised Explosive Device Disposal; RAOC personnel prior to service in Northern Ireland, the Royal Engineers, Royal Navy and Royal Air Force. All service personnel who are licensed by the RAOC to deal with IEDD are required to undergo relicensing tests once or twice every year. A technician who shows exceptional technical and professional qualities and is well experienced can be licensed for a year; most have to undertake the tests every six months.

The tests are carried out at various locations in Britain and each candidate, regardless of rank, has to perform four tasks; it could be a letter bomb, car bomb, underground cache or whatever the examiner can design and evolve. The idea is not to catch the student out but to ensure that he is technically capable. Anyone who forgets the normal examination nerves and does the job as trained is highly unlikely not to be relicensed. Some candidates get so nervous at the 'exam' they forget the 'Standard Operating Procedures' and go totally mindless, even though they might have served a tour in Northern Ireland. A sympathetic word more often than not restores the correct balance and the test is satisfactorily concluded.

The Badge

The badge by which an Ammunition Examiner was recognised originally comprised the letters AE surrounded by a wreath, white on khaki. In 1948 a competition was organised to design a new badge. Despite an entry of around 250, Brigadier Lonsdale, the Director of Land Service

Ammunition, was not satisfied. A young officer on his staff was then required to come up with an acceptable design over the weekend.

This badge owes its origins to the logo of Elizabeth Arden Cosmetics and the imagination and design skills of young Phelps (later Major General and Director of Ordnance Services). It was an impressive red, black and gold flaming grenade approximately 3in high by 2in wide with the letter A in the body of the grenade. Perhaps his skills then helped him in this successful career. His design achievement will be remembered by all who wear his badge with pride.

As has been explained, the traditional name for those within the Royal Army Ordnance Corps was 'Ammunition Examiner'. However in 1956 it was felt that with the introduction of guided missiles and the increasing work involving terrorist bombs, the title no longer reflected the true role or status of either the officer or the soldier. Officially, in those days, only those below the rank of sergeant wore a trade badge. In 1956 the Army Dress Committee gave authority for all Ammunition Examiners of the rank of sergeant and above to wear the AE badge as a badge of appointment. In 1960 the new title of Ammunition Technical Officer (ATO), replaced that of Inspecting Ordnance Officer (IOO) and Ammunition Technician (AT) that of the old AE. At this stage officers were not permitted to wear the trade badge.

In 1970 it was decided that the present small badge would be introduced, again a flaming grenade in red, black and gold and that for the first time officers would be permitted to wear it. The ammunition technicians made sure that they all had a good supply of the old and more impressive large badge and thereafter continued to wear it. With considerable good sense, the powers that be agreed that the two badges could continue, the original large plus A for other ranks and the new small grenade without A for officers.

Defence Explosive Ordnance Disposal School (DEODS)

DEODS is the tri-service training school for those who deal in explosive ordnance disposal. The school is administratively supported by the Royal Engineers. However, it is designed to meet the specialist needs of all three services and is staffed by members of the Royal Navy, Royal Air Force, Royal Engineers and Royal Army Ordnance Corps, together with a small civilian support staff. In 1993 there were also members of the United States Navy on the staff. It is one of only two NATO-approved EOD training centres, the other being located in the USA. The post of Officer Commanding is currently held in turn by an officer from each of the services, at lieutenant commander level.

Prior to 1959 each service was responsible for training its own personnel in the specialist task of bomb disposal. In those days this really meant the disposal of aircraft bombs and was a continuation of the training that had proved necessary from the 1940 period. In 1959 a joint team was established to look into the feasibility of the amalgamation of the training of the Royal Air Force and the Royal Engineers EOD training at one single location. This study resulted in the establishment of the school on 1 January 1959 at Broadbridge Heath. The Royal Navy continued to train their own personnel and, as far as they were concerned, the school was only responsible for specialist training of a short duration on dealing with the disposal of aircraft bombs for Royal Navy personnel.

In 1962 the Navy applied to participate fully in the school and accordingly RN personnel joined the training staff and command of the school then rotated between all three services. In July 1966 the 'Joint Services Bomb Disposal School' as it was then known moved to Kent and the officer commanding became just that, having previously been known officially as the Chief Instructor. This was similar to the change and improvement in status that occurred at the RAOC School of Ammunition some years previously.

Further improvements in the training programme and the status of the school followed over the years. 1968 saw the responsibility for training Royal Navy personnel in mine identification and disposal move to the school, with an increase in RN instructors. 1968 also saw the introduction of a standard NATO EOD course. The first of these was held in November 1969.

1 April 1970 saw the change of name from the Joint Services Bomb Disposal School to the perhaps more appropriate Defence Explosive Ordnance Disposal School (DEODS). A further small but important change took place in 1973 when the responsibilities of each of the services for the disposal of Improvised Explosive Devices were reviewed

and the present guidelines were laid down. At this time the establishment of instructors was increased to include two RAOC specialists.

The responsibilities of the school now include the training of selected students, not only in conventional bomb and mine disposal but also in improvised explosive devices (but excluding RAOC personnel) for war service but at present excluding Northern Ireland. Students come not only from regular and reserve personnel from the Royal Navy, Army and Royal Air Force but also Commonwealth, NATO and other friendly foreign countries. In addition police and civil defence personnel are trained in reconnaissance and recognition of unexploded ordnance.

The staff at the school was, in 1993, increased by approximately one third, to ensure that it could more properly undertake its chartered roles of projects, trials, research and technical exploitation in the field of EOD. Due to the ever increasing demand being made on the school, not only from within the UK but from abroad, for this very specialised training, the facilities of the school are now very stretched and further expansion and extensive improvements to facilities are currently under way.

Although frequently discussed and as frequently discounted, perhaps the time is coming for the training of all services, including the RAOC (since 1993 The Royal Logistics Corps) to be undertaken not at the school but at a greatly enhanced 'College'. This may be an area that can maximise the profit potential from the demands made for training by other friendly nations. After all, the services in the UK are the most experienced in the fields of conventional and improvised Explosive Ordnance Disposal.

The DEOD School at present organises in excess of 50 training courses, covering over 21 different aspects of the work for over 600 students each year; currently around 17 per cent of students are from overseas. These courses range from Elementary Explosive Ordnance Disposal through Intermediate to Advanced EOD; they vary from seven to less than one week. Part of the seven-week Tri-Service Advanced EOD course includes a two-week module for transition to war (TTW). Before potential students from the Royal Navy, Royal Engineers and Royal Air Force attend the Army School of Ammunition for their three-week Intermediate or Advanced IEDD Course they attend a one-week introductory course at DEODS. Team No. 2s also attend a two week IEDD Equipment Handling Course at DEODS.

One of the courses at the school is of two and a half days' duration and is organised from time to time for range officers to cover the correct procedures for the detonation of unexploded ordnance on firing ranges. This is a very important activity that is sometimes treated with less respect than it should, by those who use the ammunition, be it infantry or tank crews. After any live firing there are likely to be shells and bombs that fail to function for one reason or another. Someone has to go round and dispose of the 'misfires' in safety.

There is a true story of a member of a most famous Highland Regiment that had been on mortar training; a number of misfires which this chap carefully collected together in a heap fitted the explosive charge and detonator with a length of fuze. 'Shut up! I have done this for years'. As he was about to light the fuse when a brave soul, not from the same regiment, pointed out that in error he was trying to light an instantaneous fuze instead of safety fuze... If he had succeeded he would never have worn a kilt again!

EOD Technical Information Centre (EODTIC)

The vast amount of different types of explosive ordnance cannot be imagined. The modern service has tended to standardise equipment for simplicity of supply. At the start of this century every nation had its own type of ammunition, from the enormous gun of the Royal Navy battleship, down to small arms ammunition. The Second World War saw dramatic changes to air warfare, from small bombs simply dropped by hand to the massive bombs and V-weapons developed by 1945.

The problem today is that ordnance from the First World War is still around, buried in the ground or sitting on someone's mantelpiece as a souvenir. What is it? What will it do? How dangerous is it? There was an obvious need to establish an organisation to hold technical EOD information and the expertise to pass this information to authorised enquiries. Although the principle was established in the late 1960s it took until late 1975 before the idea was turned into reality and the Information Centre was finally opened. The centre is supported by twelve nations, at present – Belgium, Canada, Denmark, France, Germany, Italy, The Netherlands, Norway, Portugal, Spain, the United Kingdom and the United States – and there is a Custodian and staff of three.

The number of enquiries dealt with by the Centre has grown steadily over the years, from 150 in 1976 to 573 in 1984; some enquiries might take a few hours' work to resolve, others may take several weeks of research. The scope of the Centre covers six main headings, Land Ordnance, Aerial Weapons, Underwater Weapons, Weapon Components, Improvised Explosive Devices and Miscellaneous, which includes all EOD equipment, organisation, training, history and procedures. The main asset of the Centre is the reference library which now exceeds 2,500 separately catalogued publications and folders the earliest of which was published in 1870.

Presently, the success rate in positive response to enquiries from members exceeds 98 per cent which indicates the breadth of knowledge and experience at the Centre. The use of modern metal detectors by the general public continues to produce enquiries from the strangest sources.

EODTIC is an essential part of the 'equipment' required by and available to the technical expert and a further example of the United Kingdom's lead in the field.

CHAPTER 4

AFTER THE SECOND WORLD WAR

Following the end of the Second World War a very considerable amount of ammunition had to be collected, sorted, inspected, removed and disposed of, a task largely undertaken by the Royal Army Ordnance Corps although it must be borne in mind that the entire EOD task is shared between all the services, and is not limited to the RAOC, even in the Army. Some 600,000 tons of enemy ammunition and 120,000 tons of our own were dealt with over a three-year period. This was no mean achievement considering that the German stores had first to be located in depots that had been partly destroyed and field dumps established on battlefields, together with the other unimaginable places where people can hide unwanted items.

Disposal in Germany

This task was made more difficult by the demobilisation of the War Service Technical Staff, and by the impoverished state of wartime Europe. Ammunition consists of components which have a high scrap value (see also the account of the First World War salvage operations) and when faced with hunger, people tend to do crazy things to dangerous items, which create additional problems for those who follow. One unit actually had to complete the manufacturing process for some 500 tons to get it into a state where it could be safely handled and then be destroyed. Another unit approached a strange location to find a long causeway, constructed from layer upon layer of fused artillery shells.

To help with the clearance work the RAOC established a school in Denmark and trained over 100 Danish troops to enable them to clear their own country. On the ground German civilians were also trained and were used to clear some of their own problems.

Before the end of the war the armed services were primarily concerned with denial to the enemy of its ammunition and immediate battle field clearance. In simple terms this was normally achieved by the most expeditious means, an almighty bang! In addition to the 600,000 tons of explosive ordnance there were a further 130,000 tons of 'poison gas' to be dealt with. The task was complicated by the devastation that followed the advance. Aerial bombardment and artillery barrages had all helped to destroy storage depots and scatter all types of ammunition far and wide. Some was stored in forests, in salt and potash mines thousands of feet below the ground and in every conceivable location that could be imagined. Some was stored in factories ready for delivery. Some was so dangerous that it had to be destroyed where it lay.

The Allies had experience of the task before them, and well before the surrender a great deal of information was available as to the location of the major factories and depots. The collection of ammunition left on the battlefield, abandoned in roadside and forest dumps, exposed to the weather for months, tampered with and pilfered by the local population, and probably even booby trapped, presented a serious task with the risk of high casualties. A further problem was the need to control all explosive stores, in case a resistance movement developed in the occupied areas. The RAOC established eight separate Enemy Ammunition Depot Control Units (EADCUs). Each of these consisted of a headquarters and five or six mobile sections. Each mobile section had an all ranks strength of around 20 men. The location of these EADCUs became very quickly recognised by all, possibly because of the frequent, very large explosions as the high explosives were blown up, the rattle of thousands of machine-guns as small arms ammunition was burned, and the sudden glare when tons of propellant was burned, many times each day.

Originally these units consisted of only RAOC personnel, but as the rundown of manpower took effect, they were joined by gunners, infantry, sappers and pioneers, all speedily trained and, in a very short time, integrated into these first class working units. The morale of these units was always very high, despite being out on their own and usually miles from civilisation. They made the very best of their surroundings and often achieved a surprisingly high standard of comfort.

There are four main methods of disposal. By burning, demolition, dumping at sea or by breaking down and recovery of components. The method used depended on the type of ammunition and its general condition. Most chemical warfare ammunition had to be carefully transported, loaded onto old ships and taken out to sea. The ship was then scuttled and the whole lot sunk to a minimum depth of 300 fathoms. Some high explosive was also dumped at sea if it was considered safe to be transported. However, a considerable quantity was blown up.

The smaller items, such as grenades, mortar shells and so on, were destroyed by demolition. Small arms ammunition was usually destroyed by burning, up to 60 tons at a time. The burning of 60 tons of ammunition is hard to imagine. It was like thousands of machine-guns all firing at once - great joy to those involved with their heads well down! Some demolition explosives and stores were kept and were used to destroy German fortifications, poetic justice with a vengeance. Some was retained for use by the control commission for various purposes. Little was done by way of breaking down and recovery, as it had been during the First World War. In fact, because of the shortage of materials there was very little in the way of brass or copper in German ammunition.

On paper, all EADCUs were alike and differed only in the number of the unit. Their tasks were clearly the collection, control and disposal of ammunition, and yet each unit seems to have had a different role. One was situated in an almost completely cleared area and had two large, undamaged depots complete with German staff. It was mainly concerned with straightforward destruction and preparation for sea dumping. Another had its headquarters near the coast and supervised the loading of chemical warfare ammunition. One, in the Ruhr valley, completed the removal of ammunition from over 2,000 railway wagons, as well as other sites along the forest paths south of Bonn. A fourth was in Holland. Another was responsible for 90,000 tons stored over 2,000 feet underground. The final unit had to deal with a number of chemical warfare factories and to tranship the ammunition to the coast for disposal.

Trust nothing, suspect everything, be most careful when you are tired – that was the slogan for these units, but life was not without its lighter moments. One unit, in an isolated mountainous area, was the only British unit for miles. They blew up ammunition by day and arrested Germans who were caught outside after curfew; consequently they had to construct a prison in their billet. They took to their 'policing' role with gusto and also raided civilian homes suspected of stealing ammunition boxes and cordite for fuel.

A unit engaged in clearing an ammunition factory had to complete the manufacture of 500 tons of nitro-cellulose before they could take it away and destroy it. Similar problems were encountered in factories that had been producing TNT. There was one dump, in Holland, in a town market place, found to contain 2,000 tons of the most amazing mixture of ammunition, of every conceivable type and country of origin, a great proportion being armed and highly dangerous. A heap ten feet in height took three and a half months to clear, with only one minor casualty.

A detailed report in the *RAOC Gazette* of 1947 is perhaps worthy of inclusion, written by the officer in command of a small unit which comprised one officer and 20 other ranks and detached from an EADCU. He reported:

5,400 tons of ammunition destroyed by demolition
3,500 'blows' made without mishap
3 demolition grounds working daily, together with one cordite burning ground
110 outside locations cleared of ammunition

Although this is a simple summary, if a more detailed account is read, the real task that was entailed in the clearance of an open storage area, the dangers, trials, headaches, problems and physical discomfort undergone before being able to state that the job is finished can be appreciated. This is one such report:

The location was not a depot in the real sense of the word, with a fenced perimeter and guarded entrance, over which a certain amount of control could be exercised, but 5,000 tons of ammunition in open storage conditions, in stacks about 15 yards in from roads and tracks, over a widely dispersed area in the Forests Brandshof and Obernkirchen. Moreover, the public had free and unrestricted access.

In August 1945, when the Section which had previously been in charge of the depot moved out, all the ammunition was considered to be safe for transport and ready for sea dumping. But once the previous Section had gone the local civilian populace soon altered that state of affairs. Despite that a mobile patrol from the local brigade visited the depot twice daily to guard the ammunition, interference and pilfering was started on a comparatively large scale. Consequently, by early November, when I received an instruction to move my Section to Obernkirchen to take over the depot, the whole circumstances had completely changed, and it was very soon apparent that the breaking down of stacks by the locals to obtain boxes for firewood had reached such proportions that much of the ammunition would never go for dumping, but would be for local destruction by demolition. Even so, it was not at this stage envisaged that ultimately the whole depot would be for local destruction, but that was the final fate.

After settling in, the first problem confronting the Section was to dispose of the ammunition now rendered unfit for dumping. I made a detailed recce of the area and prepared a plan of it, marking clearly the ammunition lines. That plan was to be the key to our future activities, because it revealed that the depot fell roughly into three sub-areas. I decided that to establish a demolition ground in each of the three sub-areas would be the ideal. Another recce of the area with this aim in view was the next action, and although the area was heavily wooded and the nearby villages not so far away, I had soon selected three demolition grounds – one to each of three sub-areas – henceforward to be known by the Section as Nos. 1, 2 and 3 Demolition Grounds. Immediately the Section and the limited number of civilian labour, which by this time we had engaged, started busily preparing the grounds. Safety distances were measured out; warning boards in English and German made and erected; roads and tracks closed to the public by the erection of road closure barriers; dug-outs and sentry posts constructed; firing cables laid; and the grounds cratered.

Standing orders for the handling of ammunition, and Standing Orders for the demolition grounds were drawn up and all administrative arrangements completed so that by the last week in November, 1945, we were ready to start demolitions in ten prepared craters on each of the three grounds – thirty craters in all. During the time that these preparations were going on, a more detailed inspection of the ammunition revealed that so much interference had taken place that none of it could be certified safe for the journey for dumping at sea, and the decision was made that the whole stock of ammunition would be destroyed by demolition. So now the Section knew that a long programme of demolitions faced it throughout the worst part of the year. Here we were in the middle of winter, and the prospect of doing demolitions each and every day, rain, snow or shine, was, to say the least, a bit formidable and grim.

Then followed months of hard work in that time of year when conditions are most difficult. The winter was hard and the weather atrocious for weeks on end, and well we all knew it at that time. Torrents of rain; the lorries transporting ammunition; and the blows themselves all combined to churn roads and tracks through the woods and the demolition grounds, into a quagmire of mud and slush so common to demolition areas in winter time. Then followed the fog, sleet, snow and ice with the temperature often 10 to 15 degrees below zero. Often stacks of shells were frozen solid so that we could not move them until the temperature had risen and a partial thaw had set in. Icebound roads made transportation of ammunition from stacks to demolition grounds both difficult and hazardous, particularly on the very bad days when skid chains had to be used. But the Section did not stop. Each day even when conditions were at their worst – the men kept going, displaying an enthusiasm and team spirit which were both surprising and gratifying to see. It is difficult to be enthusiastic and cheerful when one's day is nearly eight hours of humping, loading, off-loading, laying and blowing ammunition in the depth of a severe winter, when your hands and feet are so frozen that you cannot feel them, and you are cold from an icy wind that even balaclavas, woollen gloves, scarves, pullovers and jerkins will not keep out. Yes – the Enemy Ammunition Depot at Obernkirchen was a bleak place last winter, and we often cursed the Boche for having put the ammunition there.

At first, as with all new babies, we had our teething troubles, and with daily problems in connection with labour and transport, our 'production figure' was approximately ten tons a day demolished. But we gained experience, improved our local knowledge, improved our methods, built up our civilian labour into a good force, stamped out absenteeism ruthlessly, and 'coaxed' the local brigade into letting us have a detachment of R.A.S.C. transport for the duration of the job, and so this figure went up until finally we were demolishing nearly sixty tons a day. And at this figure we began to see some really tangible results of our labours – quite a lot of empty spaces where before there were stacks of ammunition.

Running parallel with the clearance and the demolition programme the interference with the ammunition by the locals went on both by day and by night, and very soon there was hardly a stack which had not had some interference, either great or small. From many stacks every vestige of wooden box and wooden package was pilfered, rounds were broken down and propellant littered around, and in a short time what had been block stacks of correctly packed ammunition were now just pits full of shells, cartridge cases and fuses literally covered with propellant. They even littered the roads and tracks through the depot with ammunition, and scattered fuses and propellant in the woods as far as 300 yards from the sites of the original stacks. Many parts of the depot were a shambles, and in consequence the work of inspection prior to movement was fraught with considerable danger, while the work of transporting and subsequent demolition was both hazardous and tedious, and necessitated meticulous care and constant supervision. Not content with having broken down a stack of ammunition, stolen wooden boxes and packs and converted them into firewood, the pilferers even went to the stage of cutting off, from time to time, a few yards of our firing cables with which to tie up their bundles. So it can be well imagined that even to maintain our demolition grounds in working order was quite a task.

The 'war' against pilferers was a constant one, and we carried out our own patrols over the area at times when the official patrol operated by the brigade was not there. But it was only after getting good co-operation from the local Burgermeister and Police, and apprehending a score or so pilferers, whom we handed over to the local authority for police action, that we were able to control the situation. Even the services of the local German cinema were enrolled in the campaign against the pilferers, and on the screen at the evening show was flashed a warning to the local people, telling them of the danger their pilfering was causing, and the probability of large scale forest fires being caused by their scattering of loose propellant, and promising them severe penalties if they were caught pilfering or interfering with the ammunition.

And so the work of clearance and demolition went on throughout the winter, spring and early summer, and all of us appreciated the improvement in the weather which enabled us to replace the jerkins, 'woollies' and gumboots by the more comfortable 'shirt sleeve order'. Now the Enemy Ammunition depot in Obernkirchen is no more. The ammunition is gone, and all that remains to bear mute testimony to our work, and a good souvenir for the locals, are thirty large 'scars' on the face of the Forests Brandshof and Obernkirchen.

Happily all our blows were carried out without mishap, and in fact throughout the whole of the operations there was only one fatality – one

German civilian worker being killed when the cartridge of a round he picked up for loading on a lorry exploded.

This story of the Section's work would not be complete without reference to the other work carried out at the same time as the clearance of the depot was proceeding. In all, 110 outside locations were cleared of ammunition. In some instances the ammunition was inspected and transported to our demolition grounds at Obernkirchen for destruction there, while in others – where the ammunition was suspect or too dangerous to move – it was blown in situ. Quantities varied from a few pounds up to twenty tons, while the natures varied from 'blind' panzerwurfmine, shell and mortar bombs, to 500lb, U.X.B and two ton mines.

The strength of my Section is normally one officer plus twenty other ranks. Throughout this work demobilisation has added its quota of problems and my O.R. strength is now down to nine!' (L. W. COURTNEY)

This is a remarkable story, and yet it was repeated in very many other locations, not only in Germany, but all over Europe and the Middle and Far East. In Germany alone some 600,000 tons had to be sorted and a large proportion disposed of. In fact even today similar tasks of 'battlefield clearance' continue in the Falklands and the Gulf, and more recently, Bosnia.

Another report published in *The Daily Telegraph and Morning Post*, Tuesday 7 August 1945 reads:

SEA GRAVE OF POISON GAS

FROM OUR SPECIAL CORRESPONDENT WITH 21ST ARMY GROUP, GERMANY, MONDAY

Concentrated in a big forest covering an area of four square miles is one of the greatest stocks of poison gas in Germany. Hitler attached great importance to this devilish device, yet he was never able to use it.

I have just been to see it before it disappears from the world. The deadly cargo, carried in ships manned entirely by Germans, is to be thrown into the sea. There, 200 fathoms below the surface, it may remain intact for as many years. It is all contained in shells and ¾ inch steel takes a long time to corrode. Even on land the poison gas had been strictly isolated.

Dotted all over the forest which I visited were strongly built storage sheds, very commodious and all above ground. Many of them had thick concrete walls and mounds of earth with vegetation on them.

Trees were growing from this protective cover to provide impenetrable camouflage. To guard against storms each hut had a lightning conductor system of a most elaborate kind. In each of these sheds thousands upon thousands of gas filled shells were lying horizontally in wooden frames.

There is ample evidence of Hitler's preparations to use gas. An important extension had just been completed. This was a tremendously strong structure consisting of a poison gas filling station with 10 enormous containers each capable of holding many thousands of gallons.

> Brand new shell-filling apparatus, each vital part being distinctively coloured to guard against any dangerous mistake, was ready for operation in a long well ventilated room. The numerous vacuum filling machines, with empty shells in position below, left one in no doubt of the high speed at which the work could be done. The plant looked as if had just failed to come into use because of the war's end.
>
> Allied troops arrived to find a goods train ready to leave with supplies of the newest poison gas. This caused considerable excitement among our chemists. At once they probed the secret. They convinced themselves that the new gas was exactly the same as one they evolved experimentally two years ago. It had been rejected because it was inferior to kinds in use.

The same sort of situation applied in every theatre of war. For example, in Italy 100,000 tons were loaded out of the country and some 7,000 tons destroyed either by demolition or dumping at sea; in Gibraltar some 6,000 tons were destroyed.

Disposal in the UK

To give the reader an idea of the total scale, by early 1946, the total quantity in storage in the United Kingdom was around two million tons. The total capacity of the five major Central Ammunition Depots was only about one third of this figure; the balance was held in very temporary wartime locations that had to be returned to their rightful owners. Over one million tons was disposed of by the laborious process of demolition in North Wales, or by dumping at sea from Barry and Cairnryan. For the less pleasant chemical warfare shells these were loaded onto old cargo ships which were then sailed out into the Atlantic and sunk. Over a two-year period around 100,000 tons and seventeen ships met their fate in this way.

Reports on the work of No. 1 Explosives Disposal Unit in 1945 perhaps also indicate the strange experimental activities that helped with a most difficult task.

No. 1 Explosives Disposal Unit, RAOC, was formed early in 1945 in the anticipation that many thousands of tons of ammunition would have to be disposed of at the end of the war and that the Corps would be asked to undertake this task.

The pioneers of this specialised job had much experimental work to do, many amusing incidents and quite a few hair-raising moments. They chose one of the bleakest, loneliest and wettest parts of Wales out of sheer consideration for the ear-drums of the civil population. Even so, the police in Dolgelly telephoned Trawsfynydd one day to ask what had happened. Twenty miles separate the two places. What had happened was that 37 tons of No. 75 grenades were detonated to see what it felt like a thousand yards away. It felt bad.

On another occasion, 500 six-inch howitzer shells were successfully detonated in a stack with the exception of one. The physical shock and the air disturbance were incredibly violent at 800 yards. American and Naval officers observing these trials and armed with cameras of all sizes, remained flat on their fronts for the minute or two following the explosion. When the air was clear of whistling, humming and roaring red-hot fragments, we stood up and the colour returned to our cheeks, but at a sudden noise, more weird, more piercing than anything before and rapidly increasing in volume, all fell flat to the ground again and assumed the appearance of a particularly unhealthy bunch of anaemic patients. With a culminating roar a 6-inch shell buried itself in the ground 23 yards away. About fifteen people paced the distance and all agreed to stick to this figure. The size of the explosions today is very strictly limited. The tiles and ceilings of most of the neighbouring village of Trawsfynydd having been completely replaced, it is not the intention to use up any more of the taxpayers' money.

The EDU has another responsibility which it carries out at Cairnryan in Wigtownshire. This is dumping explosives at sea. It is not a spectacular task but it is laborious, sometimes dangerous and often unpleasant in winter.

In both spheres the Unit has shown a keenness and a devotion to duty which is most inspiring.

When the *Miervaldis* sailed from Barry on 20 September to be scuttled in the Bay of Biscay, she carried the last load of chemical warfare ammunition to be disposed of under arrangements made by the Ministry of Transport. The *Miervaldis* was the seventeenth ship used for this purpose, and her load of 1,880 tons brought the total disposed of in this way to nearly 100,000 tons.

The ammunition with which these ships were loaded was in the hands of the Service Departments and the Ministry of Supply. To ensure that it would not return to the surface when the ships were scuttled, all hatches were securely battened down. The Sea Transport Division of the Ministry of Transport was responsible for this work, and for the actual loading of the ships. The positioning and fixing of the scuttling charges was a joint Sea Transport and Admiralty responsibility.

The vessels selected were either too old for further service or needed repairs at a cost out of all proportion to their usefulness. There had been sixteen previous scuttlings.

The Explosion in Savernake Forest in 1946 and Other Incidents

This entire rundown was beset with problems, the worst of which was the explosion in Savernake Forest on 2 January 1946.

It was a bitterly cold winter's day with half-frozen soldiers loading American and German ammunition onto a train. Alongside was a fully laden train of 96 wagons. Suddenly and without any warning there was a blinding flash and two railway wagons and a lorry literally disappeared, fire swept around the area and more wagons burst into flames. 100,000 tons of high explosive was liable to detonate. The railway line had been cut by the first explosion so there was no way of moving wagons right out of danger, wagons had to be manually moved up and down the line, loaded lorries had to be driven out of danger, and of course the many fires had to be tackled. Shells that had been blown into the surrounding area exploded, cordite in other wagons caught fire, water in the hoses froze. By now night had fallen and the chaos and terror can only be imagined. During the various explosions some 29 railway wagons and their contents had exploded, ten had completely disappeared, of the rest only various fragments remained, of two lorries only the gear-box of one was found.

In the cold light of day there were two large craters, one some 75ft x 30ft x 14ft deep, the other 90ft x 40ft x 20ft deep. Eight men had been killed and six others injured. For the leadership and great bravery shown, the following awards were subsequently made:

George Cross	Major K. A. Biggs, Staff Sergeant Rogerson
George Medal	Sergeant D. A. Key, Sergeant J. H. Matthews (Royal Pioneer Corps)
MBE for Gallantry	WO F. W. Goodman
BEM for Gallantry	Corporal A. J. Adams, Privates F. Burnell, D. Gallagher and J. W. Prendergast
US Bronze Star	Major K. A. Biggs

Not all Ammunition Examiners were involved in incidents as spectacular as these just outlined; many worked on throughout the UK, at the large and small ammunition depots as well as on detachment to the various headquarters and Commands.

An eminent, now retired, member of the trade during the immediate post-war period was attached to Western Command; he recalls days spent dredging old German bombs from the docks in the north-west and blowing them up on the shoreline, collecting bombs from the local fishermen who had caught them in their nets, a regular occurrence, again to be blown up without any fuss on the shore. He recalls a point when he lived in his own house when his wife had as much knowledge as he did. If the police telephoned she told them what to do until the expert arrived home. He even used to keep assorted explosive items in his garage awaiting collection and disposal. Once the police asked if his neighbours kept moving; perhaps they had no idea of what was in the boxes in the corner under an old sack.

Another incident is well recalled and probably by more AE's than will regularly admit the error of their ways. The 3.7-inch heavy anti-aircraft gun was used in massive numbers during the war, the ammunition was of the fixed variety; that is, like a rifle round, with the shell and cartridge case one unit, altogether over 3ft long. In order to split the two components pressure had to be applied from side to side on the shell to remove it carefully from the case. The loose cordite had then to be removed, the shell set aside for deep sea dumping and the cordite for burning. The case then had to be turned upside down ensuring that the open end was supported on two bricks, and the primer hit with a hammer and 'nail'. This went 'pop' and the gunpowder in the primer burnt very rapidly. The brass case was then sent for scrap.

If many hundreds of these had to be dealt with, once and only once, the AE would not put the open end of the case on the bricks. If it was on the ground there was just enough force in the gases generated by the primer to lift the case into the air and usually it caught the AE under the chin. The older generation of AEs can be spotted by the scar.

Further more serious problems were caused by the 40mm ammunition. The fuse used was made of Mazak, an alloy that was very prone to corrosion. This was to such a degree that some of the smaller depots in the UK spent months carefully opening boxes, extracting rotten, damp cardboard sleeves to find a piece of ammunition with the fuse totally rotted away, exposing the steel striker and spring all ready to go bang. This was not a pleasant task at the best of times but to carry out this task in poor conditions in the middle of winter was appalling.

One more incident resulted from a call-out to the docks in Birkenhead. A Venezuelan frigate had arrived for a major overhaul and there seemed to be some sort of blockage in one of the gun barrels, so off went the intrepid specialist. It proved to be a shell that had got stuck stuck in the barrel. The blockage was eventually removed but the gun was not much use afterwards.

CHAPTER 5

OVERSEAS 1945–1972

This chapter concerns the fight against terrorism in Britain's overseas territories and the development of the techniques for neutralising or disposing of terrorist improvised devices. In the post-war period the British Empire, those large red areas on the old atlases, still covered a large part of the world. There were not many places that British troops were not stationed. In most of these postings was a detachment of the RAOC with its resident ammunition staff. For the young and old soldier it was an incredible opportunity to see the world.

The problem was that most of the countries had decided that life would be better with self rule, and really who could blame them? Terrorism is now a means of obtaining political recognition or at least this is the ethic of the terrorist. So far as the Royal Army Ordnance Corps was concerned the first experiences were in Palestine and Malaya from the late 1940s. Those who fought against the British forces were called terrorists. Their targets were, in the main, those of the traditional revolutionary, a somewhat subtle distinction for someone who is blown up.

Palestine 1945–1948

Little is recorded about the RAOC Ammunition Examiners' work in Palestine in the period 1945 to 1948. However as is well known there was considerable terrorist activity to ensure that the British left the area as quickly as possible. In April 1946 seven unarmed British soldiers of 2nd Parachute Brigade were shot and killed and in July the HQ of the British government and forces located at the King David Hotel was blown up with international publicity. The RAOC had a major problem in removing the remaining ammunition and explosive stores in 1948 and it is recorded that not all vehicles safely negotiated the route, some being blown up by terrorists en route.

Malaya 1945–1948

The main ammunition depot was based on Singapore Island at Kranji and for most of the period the main activity was normal receipt, storage and issue of ammunition to the forces actively involved in pursuing the terrorists. An ancillary but very important task was the disposal of ammunition and explosives left behind after the defeat of the Japanese.

So far as the disposal of ammunition was concerned it should be remembered that early in 1942 before the occupation of Singapore, large scale demolition took place to prevent useful items falling into the enemy's hands. During the occupation the Japanese did little to clear up the mess, in fact really they made it worse. One of their economy measures was to establish a number of factories to convert British ammunition to Japanese types and a number of explosions occurred, adding to the confusion.

In order to contribute to the rehabilitation of the island and for the general safety of the inhabitants a major clean up started in September 1945, continuing until December 1948 and thereafter over many years, as additional finds were made, during the major rebuilding of the city. A log that was prepared in 1945/46 showed over 100 locations on the island that contained significant quantities of unserviceable and unstable ammunition.

The responsibility for clearance work during this period was clearly defined. The Royal Air Force was responsible for clearance of dumps situated within the boundaries of their airfields and camps. The Royal Navy had a similar task in their depots. Probably the most difficult for the Navy was the clearance of 36 tons of gelignite in an advanced stage of decomposition from the underground storage chamber at the Naval fuel oil store on one of the small islands. The entire task had to be very carefully handled; small quantities of around 50lb batches were loaded onto stretchers, carefully transported and then burnt, over 1,600 journeys. The Army had to deal with all that remained, including aircraft bombs that were found outside airfield boundaries.

The main method of disposal was dumping at sea, the majority being sent to visit Davy Jones at a minimum of 250 fathoms. If you consider that in just over 12 months some 60,000 tons was disposed of, the logistics must have been a complete nightmare, not only the disposal but collecting the wretched stuff together. For instance the magazines at Changi with its 15-inch guns, one had been demolished in 1942, the other two just collapsed and so 100 tons of ammunition had to be extracted from under reinforced concrete. Not an easy task. The entire project was fraught with problems, not least of which was the attitude of the local population, ever careless of fire. They caused around 150 tons of bulk explosive to blow up at Nee Soon. Fortunately a further 2,500 tons located nearby was not affected or Singapore might have become a large lake.

By the end of November 1946 the main operation had been successfully concluded, though small finds continued to be made as the island was redeveloped during the following years.

I can recall one specific incident in the early 1950s. During the excavation of the foundations for a new block of flats the remains of a field gun were uncovered, complete with gun crew somewhat rotted and clothing a bit tatty, and heavily corroded ready-for-use ammunition. The ammunition was quickly collected and conveyed to Davy Jones.

The local population had become more adept over the years at removing explosives from their service containers, be they shells or bombs, using the contents in a somewhat unlawful fashion. Fishermen found explosives improved their catches and, of course, the terrorist could make good use of whatever came his way. Any find no matter how large or small and no matter where located had to be cleared and properly disposed of.

Malaya 1948–1960

This was a different situation historically. The terrorists were, in the main, Chinese. Men and women had been trained and equipped by the Allies as resistance fighters during the war. These forces by 1945 had become tough, ruthless and dedicated followers of the harsh discipline of communism. Once Japan had surrendered they were all armed and ready to liberate Malaya for the communist cause. A state of emergency was declared in 1948 which finally ended in 1960. Although the 'troubles' did not last for the full 12 years, and did not cover the entire country, a person serving was classed as being on active service and came home with the General Service Medal, clasp Malaya.

I spent an enjoyable three plus years based at Kranji, 1952 to 1956, partly on routine inspection, partly in the repair factory and partly in charge of the returned ammunition group. The main task of this department was preparing items for disposal. Ammunition returned by the infantry, after their tour of duty was completed, had to be sorted, unopened cases usually returned to stock and all opened cases usually disposed of. The life of most ammunition was limited once the seals were broken especially in the humid climate of Malaya. The usual carefree infantry attitudes meant that all hand grenades had to be checked; frequently detonators were found in place.

Life was not without military amusement nor ammunition incidents. As a corporal I had the dubious honour of being fitted out in white tropical dress and appearing on the Coronation Parade in 1953. A young officer who was in charge had the habit of poking people with his swagger stick during the training drill; imagine his horror when finally issued with a sword and forgetting and continuing to jab at the soldiers.

The Royal Artillery kept us all very active supplying 25-pounder ammunition to blast away into the jungle. I don't know if they ever accounted for a terrorist but they certainly used thousands of tons of ammunition. At one stage a series of premature explosions of the shells resulting in the gun barrels splitting like bananas, and the death and injury of a number of gun crews was traced back to a fault in the fuses, number 117. You can well imagine the chaos, all shells were recalled, fuses removed, tested, replaced and returned for use.

There seemed to be a slight problem, with the original instructions from Greenford (HQ Amm Org) which stated that all fuses had to be drop tested from a height of 7'6". This meant dropping them down a drain pipe onto concrete; if they didn't go bang they were considered OK. Trouble was that after a fall of this distance a lot just broke, second memo from London, delete 7'6" insert 3'6", back to square one! This little job kept one of my colleagues occupied for months operating a wonderful Heath Robinson arrangement of tubes and wires. Ammunition staff had to have had a childhood well equipped with Meccano to enable them to cope with service life.

Another little incident comes to mind, perpetrated by a young captain. A quantity of 3.5-inch anti-tank rockets came my way; although only practice rounds they had the full propellant charge in the tail. Great wonderment to my boss. 'I wonder how far into the ground one of these would go', says he! Being a young, well trained and obedient sergeant, I satisfied his curious mind, dug a hole, connected up the wires to a battery and he did the dirty deed. Though we dug deep, we never found the rocket, it probably ended up in Australia; what a bang! I suppose the brass thought part of the depot had exploded and what a verbal thrashing we received. The young captain was later awarded the George Medal, though for an unrelated incident!

Whilst clearing the Malayan jungle, to develop plantations, and so on, it was not unusual to find unexploded shells and bombs. Bear in mind that all services had had a great deal of fun firing or dropping these items over a considerable period of time. One poor staff sergeant was sent out to get rid of a 5.5 inch shell found during the clearance work. Some time later he telephoned HQ to advise that he could not complete his task. On enquiry he advised that the shell was stuck up a tree (it was a very tall tree) and the fuse was exposed. In the best service fashion HQ told him to acquire whatever equipment was necessary, ladders rope and the like, and get the job completed. Some would have used plastic explosive and half a mile of fuse or at least a rocket launcher but very reluctantly this poor NCO returned to the tree and got the job done. No doubt wishing he was more agile and fitter, and had kept off the Tiger Beer.

One of the main problems with ammunition and explosives in Malaya was caused by the climate. The high humidity tended to rot everything in sight, your boots and clothing as well as ammunition and explosives. Some items in regular use by the infantry such as small arms ammunition had a life span of only several months. Some explosive stores such as guncotton once the container was open had to be used or destroyed in a matter of weeks. The disposal of unserviceable ammunition continued. We had an incinerator made of sand-filled ammunition boxes with a thick steel sheet on top. In this we built a fierce fire from old wooden boxes, and down a concrete pipe fed handfuls of small arms ammunition to burn it, a safe way of getting rid of rubbish, until you go off for tea and leave a young lance corporal in charge. Although he disagreed I know he put several boxes down the pipe in his haste to be away. The concrete feed pipe travelled like a rocket for several hundred yards, the steel sheet flew like a kite into the distance followed by the ammunition box walls; again a bit of verbal abuse for all concerned.

The getting rid of smoke-generating ammunition which contained white phosphorous was an interesting exercise. Once the container had been declared unsafe it had to be stored in water until such time as it could be dumped at sea, this being the only safe method of permanent disposal. It had to be very carefully handled as if you inadvertently got a bit on your skin it burnt and burnt and burnt, causing no end of inconvenience. The only treatment, apart from amputation was a mixture of soft soap and copper sulphate, a dreadful green slimy mess.

Commercial explosives are often manufactured to a standard below that required by the military. I recall having to collect a small box containing blasting gelignite from a local mine. There were about 30 small tubes of waxed paper about 4 inches long by about ¾ inch in diameter, packed in sawdust. The entire contents were soaked in an oily liquid that indicated they were in a highly dangerous condition. Very carefully the box was removed, and cautiously transported back to the depot where it was placed in a store for safety until the next day when it was due for demolition. Due to the unstable nature of the explosive I had the job of picking it up. I always had a horror of snakes, so imagine my terror when I picked up the box and a snake slithered across both wrists. I dropped the box and fled, stood shivering outside and realised what I had done; several more cold spells then back in with a torch, check for more surprises and get on with the job.

One problem that I can well recall was due to the holding of large quantities of 155mm gun ammunition, primarily intended for Korea. The propellant charge for this ammunition was contained in a fabric bag about a yard long by some six inches in diameter. Due to adverse climate conditions these bags had become rotten; when you picked one up you tended to end up with an arm full of cordite, just like spaghetti. As the Royal Artillery could not be expected to shove the stuff into the guns by the handful it was decided to get rid of a large quantity. The way you dispose of cordite is by burning. You lay it in long rows hopefully in line with the current wind, light one end so that the whole row burns slowly into the wind. Several rows at a time, several burns a day, between each burn the Army fire brigade would thoroughly wet down the entire area with hosepipes. As you can imagine all went well for a number of days; regrettably a degree of over-confidence pervaded the burning ground. Yours truly was laying out the third or fourth burn when the cordite suddenly burst into flames, just as the wind changed. A new world sprint record was established. Then, and now, one of the qualities looked for in potential members of the trade is the ability to go from a sitting start to complete at least 100 yards in around 5 seconds, whilst being in the worst possible physical condition and suffering from a hangover.

Another problem encountered when dumping ammunition at sea is boxes that float. Prior to dumping, all ammunition was unpacked, holes were scientifically made in the boxes with a pick axe, the ammunition then repacked and shipped off. If a box floated then it was usual to fire at it with a rifle until sufficient new holes had been made to do the trick. Another less orthodox method was to let a good swimmer over the side to hold the box down until it sank. The lads loved this break from routine until one idiot got cramp, 'Help I've got cramp' came the plaintive plea. How the hell do you manoeuvre a large landing craft tank, to try and pick him up from the bow ramp? The NCO skipper of the LCT had had a nasty fright and felt a report was necessary. The poor old ammunition examiner in charge received a severe reprimand some days later. The then CO of the depot at Kranji always referred to his ammunition examiners as his 'Young gentlemen'; this was one who was regraded a 'Young Hooligan'.

Apart from the normal and abnormal military duties an AE or AT must be prepared to give expert evidence in court, military and civilian; the following is the account of one such incident which occurred in 1956, as reported in Malaya's *Straits Times.*

SURPRISE AT 'LIVE DETONATOR' COURT MARTIAL

IT'S SO DANGEROUS, SAYS EXPERT

SOLDIER ACCUSES A COMRADE

An explosives expert told a Singapore court-martial yesterday that he was not allowed to produce a detonator as a court exhibit because it was too dangerous.

Sergeant P. Birchall was giving evidence at the trial of Private Patada bin Ali, 29, of the RAOC who pleaded not guilty to charges of stealing a quantity of No. 33 electric detonators from No. 443 Base Ammunition Depot on two occasions last September.

Sergeant Birchall produced a dummy detonator to show the court what it was like.

Sergeant Birchall said 2,500 electric detonators were missing from boxes in the unserviceable ammunition store on September 26. He found that the lock on one of the doors had been forced.

I WAS GIVEN $230 SAYS WITNESS

Private Omar bin Mohammed, who admitted he had pleaded guilty to the theft of the detonators last December, when he was sentenced to two years' jail, alleged that Patada was one of four soldiers who stole the detonators. He claimed that Patada sold the detonators to a Chinese at Bukit Panjang. Omar was given $120.

Omar also alleged that Patada told him he had returned to the store and taken two more boxes of detonators.

Private Mohammed Said bin Pendek, who was charged with Omar but released when the prosecution offered no evidence against him, said he went to the store with Omar and Patada but he denied any knowledge of the theft.

THEFT DENIED

He said that Patada gave him $230 after visiting a Kampong at Bukit Panjang but he did not know what it was for.

Patada denied stealing the detonators or selling them. He also denied giving money to either Omar or Mohamed.

In a statement read in court, Patada accused Omar and Mohamed of lying about the theft to put the blame on him. Hearing continues today.

The incidents involving the conventional terrorist device were not too apparent in the 1950 period; most attacks were on more military lines, a number of people attacking an isolated rubber plantation or tin mine, or an ambush in some isolated location. The progression of safety aids was not inconsiderable: large private American cars with armoured windows and drop-down steel sheets over the windscreen, sandbag-protected houses with fences and lights, as well as assorted personal arms for the civilian population. It was strange indeed to see the planters' wives, in their best dresses, carrying revolvers, their husbands smartly turned out with white shirts and shorts with Sten guns. Yet most seemed to continue with their colonial life style.

As the campaign extended and the old ways of terrorism proved to be far from effective, then the change really came and the tactics well known today occurred. After the end of the main campaign in 1960 and before the British presence was finally concluded ammunition staff were very active.

Three George Medals were awarded to members of the RAOC Ammunition Inspectorate in western Malaysia. Captain T. A. L. Judge received his award for dealing with a bomb placed underneath the Malacca club. This was a time bomb, the timer being a modified wrist watch, the glass partly obscured by adhesive tape effectively concealing the possible time of detonation. Captain Judge neutralised the timer and safely disconnected the bomb, within minutes of the time set for detonation. Upon further more detailed examination it was discovered that only a hair's breadth separated an alternative short circuit of bared wires and the slightest movement could have set off the device. Captain M. D. Hall and SQMS B. J. C. Reid earned their George Medals in October 1965; again the device was in Malacca, but this one proved to be an entirely new and highly dangerous bomb, contained in a well sealed container. As a new type it was decided that it had to be made safe in order that its components and manufacture could be recorded for use by other experts in the future. For two and a half hours the two experts, under very difficult conditions in poor light, lay on their stomachs and carefully cut away sections of the metal box, taking the bomb apart piece by piece. During this exercise two anti-handling devices were exposed and made safe; the explosive content was then removed, which exposed part of an electrical circuit. Was it a timing mechanism or an anti-lift device? The removal of the explosive contents continued, the intention being to lessen the effects if the bomb should be triggered by a timer. After further intense and very delicate work an electrical anti-handling device and a timer were both neutralised and the entire bomb was then dismantled. It had contained seven pounds of high explosive, two hand grenades and incendiary material.

This sort of work is vital to ensure that all those involved can be kept informed on the changing ingenuity of the terrorist and bomb maker.

Korea 1948–1953

This was mainly an American war, as the historians will confirm, but as is known in Britain there was a very strong and effective Commonwealth Division. For our Whitehall-based experts the number of British soldiers was small and the fact that Korea was literally at the other side of the world was to a large degree overlooked. Despite these logistical problems the RAOC ammunition personnel were ever present, a tour of duty of eighteen months and the reward of two campaign medals.

There is little record of the activities of the Corps in Korea apart from mention of the Seventh Mobile Ammunition Repair Section, commanded in 1952 by Captain Peter Smythe, together with two ammunition examiners. One of their tasks was the demolition of some 200 tons of ammunition and the packaging of additional stocks of outdated or unusable ammunition for dumping at sea.

Several ex-Korea Ammunition Examiners found their way back to Singapore after their eighteen months' stint, to either complete their National Service or to complete their full three years overseas tour if regular soldiers. One I recall had been involved in a motor accident. Whilst driving a jeep at night he saw two motor cycles approaching down the road, one on either side; too late he realised it was a massive American tank transporter using very dim lights to avoid detection by the enemy. They had to unload the tank before they could get him out of the jeep, by this time well under the trailer. I well remember the individual; for some reason he did tend to twitch rather badly at times.

Cyprus 1955–1958

On 1 April 1955 the Greek Cypriot terrorists started their all-out fight against the Government. Due to the number of incidents involving explosive devices at a very early stage it was decided to form special units of Ammunition Examiners who were then allocated to the CID at the major police stations on the island. The Inspecting Ordnance Officer in charge was located at Police HQ.

A significant development was the very close involvement and high degree of co-operation between the civilian police and the army. The police ballistics expert, Chief Inspector Bird, had served in Palestine both before and after the Second World War; apart from being a highly experienced officer perhaps he recognised the benefits of a far closer degree of co-operation than had previously existed. In any event in 1956 Major Harrison, the IOO, was officially seconded to the Cyprus government to fill the specially created post of Government Explosives Officer.

The terms of reference of those Ammunition Examiners who were attached to the regional police stations were to accompany the CID to all scenes were explosives were involved, to disarm or dispose of the explosive objects within the limits laid down, to submit comprehensive reports and to give evidence in court if required, and to identify substances subject to government control or embargo.

During the period of the emergency, some four years to the last act of terrorism on 23 December 1958 the teams dealt with a large and varied collection of bombs, grenades, pipe bombs and booby traps. Over 4,300 bomb explosions were investigated, 4,688 unexploded devices were dealt with and some 3,000 recoveries of arms, ammunition and explosives were recorded.

Two AEs were regrettably killed during this period whilst on duty. Sergeant R. Kilby accompanied a police patrol to investigate a number of planted home made mines; he located and made safe two and was killed by a third. He had been accompanied by Captain Greenwood who then cleared the remaining mines and identified the design as a new type previously unknown to the security forces. Staff Sergeant J. A. Culicin was killed dealing with a device at Limassol – September 1955. Following a tip-off to police a cache of explosives had been found in a hillside cave. The Staff Sergeant entered the cave and found a large wooden crate smelling strongly of almonds, the characteristic odour given off by some explosives. The Staff Sergeant then cleared the others from the cave. What occurred next is not really known, but there was a massive explosion which killed the Staff Sergeant.

There were, as usual, a number of incidents that were slightly 'out of the ordinary'. An EOKA agent placed a bomb in Government House, actually under Field Marshal Harding's bed. In order to provide evidence it was necessary for the IOO to defuse the device and make it safe. All went well and thankfully the Field Marshal was able to re-occupy his bedroom. I wonder for how long after he continued to look under his bed before he retired for the night!

After the end of the emergency it was reported that 'Throughout the campaign the sense of duty of the IODs and AEs was always of the highest order and they were prepared to take on any task, however hazardous, by day or night, despite the casualties among their ranks. It is a tribute to their skill and efficiency that casualties have not been higher.' In recognition of the service the following awards were made:

MBE (Gallantry)	Captain J. W. Greenwood
George Medals	Major W. C. Harrison, Staff Sergeant F. G. Giblett, Sergeant J. T. Proudlock, Sergeant A. Taylor
BEM (Gallantry)	Sergeant R. P. Goad, Sergeant R. W. MacDonald

Perhaps the most significant achievement of the Cyprus campaign was that during this period the first RAOC Bomb Disposal Unit was established and the pattern was set for their future involvement in the forensic investigations of criminal or terrorist incidents in which explosives were used.

Borneo 1962–1966

This was a little-reported war, never officially a war but a period of considerable activity and intensity in the most difficult conditions. Again the insurgents can only be classed as terrorists even though they were

Indonesian regular soldiers. However, as the conflict progressed significant numbers of Chinese Communists became involved.

There was a continuing requirement during the entire period to deal with terrorist devices and with the large number of explosive missiles found, including aircraft bombs, many dating from the 1939–1945 period. As the resources of the Navy, Royal Air Force and Engineers were very limited, to say the least, the task of investigating, identifying and disposing of these items fell on the RAOC Ammunition Examiners. In February 1966 Staff Sergeant Lowe dealt with one 500lb and three 250lb bombs, six 60lb rocket heads and a 100lb incendiary bomb, and at the same time undertook his more mundane and routine tasks.

Aden 1964

Many readers may recall the Colonel of a Scottish regiment who got totally fed up with the terrorist activities in Aden, sent his men in to sort it out and as a result decided to take early retirement. His popularity in the UK resulted in his election as a Member of Parliament.

The development of the 'come on' tactic was significant in Aden. A frequent method was to plant a bomb, when the troops and the ammunition staff arrived to investigate, toss a grenade or two amongst them. The old faithful 36 (Mills) grenade was still causing havoc even after half a century.

In this relatively small theatre of conflict one officer dealt with over three hundred explosive devices during his tour of duty, daily risking his life, a very strange breed of men. A total of approximately 700 'bombs' were dealt with during the period.

In every terrorist campaign many were killed when making, transporting or laying and arming their bombs. The trained professional was much more likely to survive than the ignorant terrorist, even though the equipment available to the professional was woefully inadequate. In the early days your kit would fit into a shoe box (or more usually an old ammunition box), scissors, wire cutters, surgical scalpels, string, fish hooks and the ever-present sticky tape; not very sophisticated when dealing with electronic devices. Fortunately science, innovators and the aptitude of the trade soon produced additional equipment. These days you need a large van to carry it all round in.

During the period November 1964 to December 1965 Major J. F. Elliott personally investigated 189 reported incidents involving various explosive devices. He dismantled 309 potentially lethal objects, of which 184 proved to contain explosives. In most cases the devices were crude and home made but many contained simple but effective anti-handling mechanisms; also a fair amount of the explosive content was decomposed and highly volatile. On 16 June 1965 Major Elliott was called to an explosion at the Officers' Mess, Middle East Command. Working by torchlight he found and successfully disarmed three explosive time charges. His task was made more difficult by the lack of adequate lighting and further unnerving by the presence of the dismembered body of the terrorist, blown up by one of his own bombs. For this and other tasks Major Elliott was awarded the George Medal in April 1966.

Major G. C. Brownlee, who succeeded Major Elliott, was also very active in the pursuit of his chosen profession. He too was awarded the George Medal, in March 1968. The citation revealed that he had personally answered over 170 calls from the civil authority to deal with explosives or suspect devices. Often under threat of terrorist attacks in the dangerous areas of Aden, he dismantled and recovered over 100 explosive items required for forensic examination. On twenty occasions he removed caches of explosives in a highly dangerous state. His final effort was to neutralise a bomb placed in a well; to have blown it up would have deprived a large area of its only water supply. He was lowered into the cramped and dark conditions of the well and successfully neutralised the bomb.

Hong Kong 1967–1968

Towards the end of July 1967 it became apparent that a major campaign had started in the territory that was beyond the capability of the local ammunition staff. Twelve unexploded devices in 24 hours caused a plea for more assistance from Singapore HQ. Once again the sophisticated equipment was not available and the operators relied on the nylon cord, hook, knife and scissors, plus a copy of the Bible for those with religious tendencies.

The devices being used mainly produced a form of low explosion. The Chinese have for hundred of years been used to producing fireworks of one sort or another, and many devices were really fireworks although of a somewhat daunting variety. The devices were not usually difficult to find; in fact many were attached to banners of one sort or another. The early way to deal with these was to fix the cord to the suspect item, retire and pull the thing about with great vigour.

One device about the size of a small shoebox caused a great deal of consternation. When approached by the apprehensive operator complete with hook, string and Bible, it suddenly moved; a step or two nearer and the wretched box moved further away, again a step, again it moved. Bugger it, if it can move it can't be that sensitive he thought as he jumped on it. A rat in a box with holes for its feet. Thank God, another hoax!

The early phase rapidly developed into stage two when a quantity of high explosives were reported stolen. All operators were then ordered to blast open all suspect devices, using a detonator and, if necessary, detonating cord. Life was starting to get very interesting for the handful of men on the ground. Never before or since had the RAOC, or for that matter anyone else, received such a volume of business; some 9,000 incidents over a seven-month period. On one day 280 bombs were reported, one warrant officer dealt with 300 devices. During this period there were some 13 RAOC operators in the Colony. The main purpose of this campaign was to cause as much chaos as possible – remember the vast number of people who live in Hong Kong. Twenty well designed and well placed devices could bring the city to a complete standstill for most of a working day.

The Chinese are probably the most inveterate gamblers in the world; imagine their distress when a bomb was found at the starting gate at the race track. The operator was called and advised that the device must be removed quickly as the first race was about to start. The first and only time 26,000 spectators watched from start to finish and rose to their feet to applaud when the task was satisfactorily completed.

Hong Kong experience brought about a considerable improvement to the equipment available to the operator. A vehicle was equipped for each team, armoured suits (police style), anti-mine goggles, special helmets, armoured vests, plus various explosive devices to blast open suspect objects from a safe distance. The days of having to go up to every device to touch and feel were on their way out.

There was one fatality during this period when Sergeant Workman was tragically killed on Lion Rock from injuries sustained during a 200-

foot fall after a booby-trapped flag exploded as he was dealing with it.

Not all those who deal with explosive devices and who are injured are necessarily injured by the device: WO1 S. G. Woods, kneeling to dismantle a device set on a traffic island in the middle of Queens Road, was regrettably run over by a Chinese motorist and received leg injuries. There is no record of what happened to the offending driver. WO1 Wood was subsequently awarded the MBE for gallant conduct for his work in the Colony.

There were other lighter moments. A young technician was called out one evening to neutralise a bomb in a house, imagine his surprise and delight to find it was a house of ill repute. His efforts were successful and he was duly offered his reward. With the greatest devotion to duty he advised the sixteen lovely young Chinese girls that he had another suspicious package to investigate. I wonder if he ever went back!

During this five-month period and the high level of activity a duty rotation system was introduced on a 12-hour basis. A team of four operators would work

(A) 12 hours on duty

(B) 12 hours on 1-hour call

(C) 12 hours on 4-hour call and

(D) 12 hours' rest

At many times these rotas had of necessity to go by the board.

As with most unknown situations close co-operation with the police was of paramount importance, and it was the responsibility of the police to get the team to the incident by the quickest and safest route. Many teams found the journey far more life threatening and stressful than the job itself.

A great deal of valuable experience was gained in Hong Kong that has proved of immense use in Northern Ireland. Small transistor batteries became the power source, light-sensitive cells, although not particularly successful, various types of time delays and relays. However, as with most terrorist devices of the time they were relatively unsophisticated, again as is common many bombers blew themselves up first.

One of the problems encountered by the technicians was the false sense of security felt after a long sequence of false and hoax incidents. In Hong Kong the RAOC met and overcame this challenge, of a type and scale never before experienced. Although the injury rate was high over a short time span, it was low in relation to the number of incidents.

Undoubtedly mistakes were made and the prevailing view was that if lessons had been learned then losses had not been in vain.

In concluding this section I must draw the reader's attention to the fact that not all bombs and explosive devices were dealt with by the RAOC. Some were handled by the Royal Engineers, some by the Royal Air Force and some by the Royal Navy, and the assistance and close co-operation of the civil Police was and is of paramount importance.

In Hong Kong, for example, Petty Officer Charlwood of the Royal Navy clearance diving team and Captain Humphries and QMS Christison BEM of the Royal Engineers were all injured on disposal duties.

Guadalcanal, Solomon Islands 1967

These islands were the scene of very bitter fighting between the American and Japanese forces in 1942. The area around Hell's Point, some 270 acres of land, about 12 miles from the administrative capital, contained an estimated 5,000 tons of assorted ammunition, scattered around and largely covered by tropical vegetation.

After the main combat zone had moved North in 1942, the Americans established an ammunition depot of some 15,000 tons at Hell's Point. A series of major explosions in the depot, over a five-day period, killed a number of people and effectively scattered the depot's contents over a very wide area.

During 1948 and again in 1953 there were a series of explosions, lasting several days which killed or injured many of the local people. Over the successive years the condition of the ammunition further deteriorated and sporadic explosions became an accepted part of life for the local population.

In 1967 it was found necessary to extend the island's main airstrip and also to recover this area of valuable freehold land. During the summer of 1967 two ammunition technicians Major H. Mitchell and WO2 H. Vaughan were sent to the island to examine and report on the problems involved in clearing the dangerous ammunition and explosives from Hell's Point and the Henderson Field extension. The report indicated that an area of some 80 square miles was endangered by large quantities of various types of ammunition, in various stages of decay. At Hell's Point in an area of 270 acres it was estimated that there were over 4,000 tons of ammunition.

Having completed the initial investigation Major Mitchell and WO2 Vaughan cleared the Henderson Field extension area to enable the airport improvements to go ahead. In a three-week period they cleared some 260 tons of ammunition, including 12,000 shells, mortar bombs, grenades and 20 tons of bulk explosive scrap, by means of demolition and deep sea dumping. Many of these items were concealed by the undergrowth, some buried just under the surface, others just lay on the ground. Fuses had disintegrated and some explosive fillings had broken down through age and climatic conditions thus becoming extremely sensitive. Some items had to be blown up where they lay, a considerable quantity had to be carefully carried away by hand, loaded onto barges and safely dumped at sea. For their exceptional work Major Mitchell and SQMS Vaughan were both awarded the MBE in 1968.

Following their appraisal of the remaining work, estimated to be four years, they recommended that a Warrant Officer AT be seconded to the colonial administration to complete the clearance. WO1 C. M. McKiernan volunteered for this operation and took up his duties on 23 June 1969 and by 30 September had disposed of 5,592 major and 1,106 minor items either by destruction in situ or by dumping at sea. With commendable energy, WO1 McKiernan systematically cleared the entire area.

Cyprus 1970–1971

Like most theatres, incidents continue long after the main hostilities have ceased. The problems tend to continue with a high degree of awareness once this has been established. In Cyprus 1970, after a relatively peaceful period a call was received by Major A. R. C. Munro and WO1 Dave Oldham to investigate a suspect device at a power station. As usual this was not at a particularly reasonable time of day, 9.00 pm to be precise on a Saturday. Off went the intrepid duo, nerves somewhat strained, their first job together. On arrival at the power station all was quiet, all personnel had been safely evacuated. Looking through a window there was a nasty-looking parcel hanging by wires from inside the switch compartment. In the best traditions of the trade time was spent in evaluating the task; the more time spent in thought the greater the belief that it was a hoax. Finally the decision was made. Willie Munro went up to the package, attached a hook to the doors of the cupboard, retired and gave a sharp tug; exposed was a mass of wires and a box full of paper. No one ever found out who was responsible and I guess the intrepid duo were just thankful to get home for a well earned drink.

Willie Munro had another task in May 1971. A report had been received at HQ that there was a suspicious package in the cellars of the British Embassy in Beirut. 'Catch the next plane and don't bother with any kit. The Americans will supply what you need.' At the Embassy and taped to a wall behind a cupboard was a small manufactured plastic box, some 6 x 8 x 3 inches, completely sealed. The box was a mass of electronic circuits but there was no sign of either a detonator or any explosives. Next step move it from the wall with great care and X-ray it again, still no problem so it was then opened up. It proved to be a sophisticated form of long distance listening device. A few days' holiday in Beirut courtesy of the Ambassador (he picked up the bill) and sworn to silence and then back to Cyprus, to more sun, sea and enjoyment. The ultimate reward was the enclosed letter.

From: Colonel APW MacLellan MBE
Headquarters, Near East Land Forces, 26th May 1971

Dear Munro,
The General has asked me to send you his congratulations on the very successful task that you completed recently in BEIRUT.
May I add my own – rather you than me!

Yours sincerely
Pat MacLellan

The *Queen Elizabeth 2*, 1972

One of the most publicised incidents ever to feature an ammunition technician occurred in 1972 when it was reported that the *QE2*, in mid-Atlantic, had one or more suspect devices on board.

The entire incident so caught the imagination that a major film was made, featuring Richard Harris. *Juggernaut* was a huge success.

The reality was equally dramatic: on 18 May at 10.00am a telephone call was recorded at Ammunition HQ requesting the services of a parachute-trained ATO or AT to deal with a bomb on a ship mid-Atlantic. Little else was known except that there were supposedly a total of six bombs on the ship set to explode at 9.00pm that day. Despite frantic efforts it was not possible to find a suitably qualified parachutist; one was in Hong Kong, one was in Northern Ireland, one was in Germany, another in Berlin. Just before noon a young Captain who was instructing in Explosive Ordnance Disposal and who, as a hobby had completed a couple of jumps, telephoned and modestly he offered 'if the Colonel wished he was willing to have a go'. By 12.30pm he was airborne by helicopter to the RAF Parachute Training School at Abingdon, dropped from the tower a time or two, taught how to drop into water, given tea and coffee and sandwiches, and by 3.30pm he was on board a Hercules aircraft with a scratch crew ready to take off.

In view of the experience as a parachutist, and remember the added difficulties of a drop into water and the water being the North Atlantic, the Ministry of Defence took the precaution of arranging for a team of experts to go along to help: a Lieutenant and a Sergeant from the Royal Marines' Special Boat Section and a Staff Sergeant from the Special Air Service, all explosive-trained and experts at landing in water.

The discussion between the ship's Chief Officer and the Ministry of Defence was by telephone and it soon became apparent that the ship was a long way from the UK; could the plane get there in time, could the team find and disarm the six bombs before the deadline of 9.00pm?

The Hercules located the *QE2* at about 8.15pm, cloud base about 200 feet, drizzle but not too bad a sea. Due to the weight of the equipment the drop had to be about 800 feet. A total of seven runs had to be made before all the team had been dropped, the run in at below 200 feet to sight the ship, then the rapid climb to 800 feet, the drop and some 10 minutes in the sea, followed by a short rough launch trip produced a rather green team of experts when they unsteadily reached the deck. The entire operation from start to finish had been successfully accomplished in about 11 hours but if the bombs had been set off at 9.00pm it was too late to complete the task. In fact it was all a massive and not very clever hoax; there were no bombs but some suspect luggage. Being a true professional Captain Williams did what was expected, blew open the suitcase and ruined someone's clothing. The next few days were most memorable for the team, treated like heroes by passengers and crew, an experience not easily forgotten.

A sequel to these events was the realisation that a similar event could easily occur again, the capability to respond must exist. Today there are a number of officers and men suitably trained and specially trained for parachuting into the sea, available. These men are located wherever ATOs and ATs of the British Army are posted.

A salutary story recounted by a member of the trade, who served in North Africa long after the end of the Second World War; one of his tasks was to make safe any old German equipment reported by the wandering nomads. One such reported a tank complete with the remains of its long deceased crew.

No one in the team was really keen to enter the tomb to remove the unused ammunition, so a few incendiary grenades dropped through the open hatch seemed to be an acceptable solution. The team then retired to the top of a nearby sand dune to watch the result. Most spectacular, until to their horror they realised there may have been one up the spout and their vantage point was in a direct line with the gun barrel. Even after many years in the heat of the desert the wretched thing still worked. Now the RAOC do not often find themselves facing the wrong end of a tank (even a dead one) let alone one which could and did still shoot. How it missed none can tell and perhaps this is the first time this embarrassing tale has ever been told. Very red faces all round and not the result of the sun.

The same AT also recalls the tale of a visit to a shed in which a collection of anti-tank mines had been stored, following collection from the desert by the local forces. Now bear in mind that these had been laid to destroy enemy tanks during World War II and it was therefore reasonable to assume that fuses had been and still were in place. The AT looked at the stack of mines, probably nine to ten feet in height. He did not need a calculator to realise that the weight resting on the lower mines greatly exceeded the pressure needed to compress the spring to detonate the mine. A sudden feeling of extreme cold, even for the time of day in the Middle East. Unless the stack was dismantled very, very carefully the result could be catastrophic. Happily, as he was able to recount the story many years later the job was completed without incident.

It is not only the Ammunition Technician who can be humorous. An AT recounts the tale of working on empty 40mm Bofors cartridge cases; you hit the primer on the base with a hammer to fire the primer, then the case can safely go for scrap. If you do this job long enough you might make a mistake. In this story one case was not empty and upon hitting it with a hammer off it went. The surgeon was heard to ask the AT patient what type of ammo it was that caused the injuries, 'Oh, 40mm', was the reply, 'Oh well', says he 'we've only found 39 bits of brass so far so will keep looking'!!

CHAPTER 6

AT HOME

The work of the Ammunition Technician was not all overseas and a few of the many incidents at home In the United Kingdom are outlined in the following extracts from newspaper cuttings of the time.

COVENTRY EVENING TELEGRAPH, 1952

'There is no unexploded bomb in Coventry Cathedral'. This was the conclusion arrived at yesterday after an inspection by experts. In the picture Captain N. T. Thurston (right), secretary of the Reconstruction Committee and the Provost, the Very Rev R. T. Howard explaining to Captain Chamberlain of the Royal Army Ordnance Corps what was found after the blitz in 1940. Two members of the Press watch the digging operations through the doorway under the vestry.

NO UNEXPLODED BOMB UNDER CATHEDRAL

There is no unexploded bomb in Coventry Cathedral - 'Tell the people that and put their minds at rest', said the Provost, the Very Rev. R. T. Howard yesterday.

His statement came after investigations had been carried out on a 1ft diameter hole in the tiled floor.

It was this hole, filled with dirt and dust and another hole in the ceiling above which gave rise to the suspicion that a bomb might have buried itself under the vestry after a raid 12 years ago.

THE VOLUNTEERS

And the man who set Coventrians' minds at ease was a small dapper Captain in the Royal Army Ordnance Corps. He was two hours late coming from Shrewsbury because of car trouble.

The first thing he did was shuffle his foot round rather vigorously on the spot. Then he asked for two volunteers, 'you and you' from the contractors working on the Cathedral to help him to dig. Then the Captain, the Provost, Captain N. T. Thurston (secretary of the Reconstruction Committee), the two workmen and a representative of the War Damage Commission, started examining the hole.

CONCRETE INTACT

Behind closed doors there was an ominous sound of earth being attacked by a pick. Ten minutes elapsed, the door was flung open and out walked the party smiling broadly.

'We have dug down and found that the concrete under the floor tiling is intact and unbroken', said Captain Thurston.

Provost Explains

Then the Provost gave his statement of explanation of the two holes.

'Early in the morning after the night of the blitz, I came with Mrs Howard to the Cathedral. On the exact spot where the ground was broken and the bomb is suspected, we saw a very large shell or small bomb lying in a broken condition.

'It was removed in the course of the days which followed. I have always believed that it was this bomb shell that made the hole in the floor above.' The Provost added that during the years since the blitz, a heavy motor grass mower had been moved consistently over the suspected spot. He himself had walked over the spot scores of times.

* * *

County Borough of Dudley
Fire and Ambulance Service

The Chief Engineer
Western Command Headquarters,
Queens Park, Chester

Dear Sir,

One of the Sub. Officers attached to this station had the misfortune to suffer serious injury whilst attending a fire in which a consignment of detonator canisters were involved. An explosion took place and in order to determine the cause, contact was firstly made with the T.A. Unit, Turners Hill, Rowley Regis, to obtain their views on the possibility that one of the canisters forming part of the consignment in the scrap yard could have been responsible for the explosion.

The canister was not readily identified by them, but I must say that they lost no time in forwarding the detonator container through the Smethwick Unit to the Headquarters, Mid West District, Shrewsbury.

The purpose of this letter is to draw attention to the prompt action taken by Captain Chamberlain of that Unit in responding to my request for assistance. He visited the site where the explosion occurred at very short notice and the observations which he made, in a quiet, unassuming way, were most helpful.

I trust that you will find some way of conveying to him my appreciation for his prompt attention in the above matter.

Yours faithfully,
Chief Officer

* * *

EVENING NEWS AND SOUTHERN DAILY MAIL - 1963

Shells Exploded in Fratton Garden

Homes cleared – then blast lights sky

More than 30 houses in the Fratton area of Portsmouth were evacuated for a short while last night when bomb disposal experts from Southern Command exploded highly dangerous shells found in Terwick Street.

At the same time, other households in the district stood in groups in the streets, the doors and windows of their homes left open so as not to be damaged by the blast. It was seconds before 10.15pm that the second blast shook the Terwick Street area – a blast that shattered a few windows and silhouetted the houses in a flash that lit the night sky.

A minute or two later, Major W. Musson, RAOC, of the Ammunition Inspectorate of Southern Command, appeared in the doorway of 11 Terwick Street and announced it was all clear – 'they can go home'. Terwick Street and Gunner Street went back to normal – lights came on in the houses, the windows were shut, the doors were bolted – and the Gunners Arms carried on serving. Like that famous London theatre in the blitz, it never closed.

It was earlier in the day that Mr Robert Stephen Thorne, a 24-year-old storekeeper, of 11 Terwick Street, came across what he took to be a shell while digging in his garden. He took it indoors to show his wife, busy coping with 18-month-old Stephen and one-month-old Jane, and then took it back into the garden and continued digging.

SECOND FIND

'A few minutes later', he told the *Evening News*, 'I came across another one, and my wife suggested that I should report it to the Police'. He did so, and in a short while, Capt J. F. F. Sharland, RAOC, also of Southern Command's Ammunition Inspectorate, arrived on the scene.

He came to the conclusion that the two shells were safe to move, and obtained permission to clear St Mary's Church playground to detonate them. But when they went back to No. 11 to fill some sand bags with the sand in which the two shells had lain hidden, others gradually came to light – until, in all, there were about a dozen, including one very badly corroded 3.7in anti-aircraft shell.

'I came to the conclusion that this one was too dangerous to move', he explained. 'It was obviously highly explosive, so I asked Major Musson to come down for a second opinion.'

While Mr & Mrs Thorne sat at home, Superintendent L. E. Cooper, in charge of the Fratton Division of Portsmouth Police, alerted the districts in his division, in case a mass evacuation was necessary.

Provided with a special police escort from Salisbury – Southern Command's headquarters – to Fratton Police Station, Major Musson did the journey in 75 minutes despite the crowded roads as Whitsun holiday-makers made their way home.

A quick inspection soon settled the issue. 'These will have to be blown tonight. They are too dangerous – even a cat could set off an explosion'.

LANDPORT BOY HELD DEATH

There was an air of excitement – but quiet efficiency – in Fratton Road police station as officers were briefed last night on the part they had to play in seeing that the families in Gunner Street and Terwick Street were evacuated.

Quiet, that was, until 13-year-old Regan Bowers of 18 Common Street, Landport, walked into the station.

'Please sir,' he said to the group of waiting Press reporters and photographers, 'I found this ...'. In his hand was a cannon shell, quite badly rusted, but still easily recognisable.

The reporters and photographers backed away, the Constable on desk duty retired to the inner room and returned with Capt Sharland.

'Could Kill You'

Quietly, never raising his voice, and looking hard at young Regan, the Captain said, 'If ever you find anything like this again, do not touch it – it could kill you at 100 yards'.

Regan who found the shell in a hole close by South Parade Pier on Sunday, told Captain Sharland, 'I think there was another in the hole.'

Could he point out the place again? Yes, he could – and he was whisked away in a bomb disposal vehicle to Southsea beach.

But the tide had ebbed and flowed and the big hole that Regan had been digging in near the pier was no longer there.

* * *

ROYAL ARMY ORDNANCE CORPS GAZETTE
April 196 Vol. 45 No. 11

Two George Medals

The *London Gazette* of the 7th February 1964, announced that Major W. Musson, RAOC, and Conductor S. Brazier, RAOC, had each been awarded the George Medal. On the 12th of October 1963, Conductor Brazier was called upon to advise and assist Major Musson, the SATO HQ Southern Command, in the removal and disposal of an unknown quantity of No. 74 Grenades (Sticky Bombs), some of which had been discovered on top of a steep grass covered bank close to a barrack area in Aldershot.

Working together as a team and using short wooden probes and paint brushes, over a period of two days, a total of twenty grenades were carried singly in a sand filled box by Major Musson and Conductor Brazier to a demolition area 160 yards away from the cache and destroyed. The balance of thirty-four grenades was destroyed where they lay, but this could not be done until an ingenious sandbag traverse was constructed.

Of World War II vintage, Grenades No. 74 are inherently one of the most dangerous weapons ever produced. These particular grenades had been in the ground for twenty or more years and were in an extremely dangerous condition. With an original storage life of only two years the chemical stabiliser must have been quite ineffective and the nitro-glycerine content highly sensitive.

The task of moving the grenades was hazardous in the extreme to the extent of imperilling the lives of both men. Both showed great physical courage, mental endurance and a technical skill of the highest order.

* * *

Gwynedd Constabulary
Chief Constable's Office, Caernarvon
13th February 1970

Major H. Chamberlain

Dear Sir,
Ref: John Barnard Jenkins and Frederick Ernest Alders
You will by now have been informed that your attendance is required at Ruthin Assize to give evidence in the above case. I am writing to inform you that your presence will not be required before the 5th March 1970, at the Assize Court, Ruthin, and that in any case you will receive a further warning of the exact day on which you will be required to attend.

Should you be in any doubt about this matter, do not hesitate to contact this office.

Yours faithfully
Detective Chief Superintendent for Chief Constable

* * *

In the County of Denbigh
Petty Sessional Division of Ruabon.

To Harry Chamberlain

You are hereby ordered to attend and give evidence at the trial of Frederick Ernest Alders and John Barnard Jenkins before the next Court of (Assize) For the County of Denbigh to be held at Ruthin, or at such other Court, place or time as you may be directed.

Clerk of the Magistrates' Court
sitting at Ruabon

Dated the 16th of February 1970
(By Order of the Court)

* * *

Gwynedd Constabulary
Chief Constable's Office
Caernarvon
5th March 1970

Major H. Chamberlain

Dear Sir,
Ref: John Barnard Jenkins and Frederick Ernest Alders
I refer to the above case and to my previous letter to you on 13th February 1970, and also to the notification you received from the police in the last few days.

The position now is that this case was mentioned at Ruthin Assize on Wednesday 4th March, and the Judge directed that it be put over to Mold

Assize. It is provisionally anticipated that the first day of hearing will be Tuesday 7th April 1970. I will, however, arrange that you receive a further communication informing you exactly of the day on which your attendance will be required.

Again, should you be in any difficulty concerning these arrangements or in any doubt at your attendance, do not hesitate to contact me.

Yours faithfully
Detective Chief Superintendent
for Chief Constable

* * *

TEN YEARS FOR MAN WHO CAUSED
HAPSFORD WATER PIPE EXPLOSION

'Wales would not approve or applaud what had been done and would condemn the terror they had contrived to spread among her people by their wicked deeds', said Mr Justice Thomason before passing sentence on the two men accused in the Welsh bomb trial at Flintshire Assizes on Monday.

'Wales will disown and disclaim such methods of promoting interests, and she will expect you to be punished for your misdeeds,' he said.

John Barnard Jenkins, aged 37, an Army Ordnance Corps Sergeant, stationed at Saighton Camp, Chester, of Grange Road, Wrexham, was sentenced to 10 years' imprisonment concurrent on the 8 charges to which he had pleaded guilty, last Friday, after changing his plea.

His co-accused, Ernest Alders, aged 21, an aerial rigger of Pearson Street, Rhos, Wrexham, was sent to prison for six years, concurrent on the same charges.

They were charged with conspiring to cause explosions at water pipelines at Llanrhaedrym-Mochnant, Lake Vyrnwy and Hapsford; of store breaking and stealing explosives; one of aiding and abetting an explosion; that hitherto both had good characters.

He said the police forces of Wales and Cheshire had been active for a long time and he asked that congratulations be communicated to these forces for the work they did.

Post-war Souvenirs

In addition to the growing threat of terrorism in mainland Britain there is the danger from war-time souvenirs that have been lying around for years or even from digging up buried 'treasure' in the garden. An increasing number of folk go trudging around with metal detectors looking for Roman gold and could easily find a bit of more recent highly explosive scrap iron.

This is no figment of the journalistic imagination. The Royal Army Ordnance Corps have teams of men permanently located at central locations through the UK. Specialists in Explosive Ordnance Disposal; they are not there solely to deal with the possible threat of a terrorist device, but also to deal with the hundred and one sundry finds reported each year by the general public.

An 80-year-old widow in Yorkshire had lovingly polished a souvenir her husband had brought back from France after the First World War; for over 60 years it had stood proudly gleaming on her fireplace – a live and deadly high explosive shell! When removed and blown up, it functioned as designed.

An estate agent listing the contents of an old gentleman's house, for sale following his death, came across a grand collection of goodies. As he had been in the army for national service he recognised the assortment of grenades, anti-personnel mines, small arms ammunition, cannon shells, fuses etc. The local Bomb Squad were called to remove and destroy them.

Even today the Royal Engineers are kept active around the country. When the foundations for new buildings are excavated, deeper than the previous buildings, it is surprising to discover how far into the ground some of the old German bombs have penetrated, especially in soft ground.

During an air raid in the south a bomb demolished a private house, which after the war, was rebuilt. Many years later the house was demolished to make way for a large high rise office block and a very large German bomb was found intact, in perfectly good working order. If it had gone off it would have caused considerable devastation. The original wartime report that it had exploded was incorrect: the bomb was so big it had demolished the house by the force of the impact and then gone far into the ground below the foundations and had lain hidden for over 40 years.

In another incident in Nottingham, the occupier of the house recalls the night in 1941 when a bomb hit the house next door. The blast caused damage to his roof which had to be repaired. In his old age in the early 1990s it was decided to improve the insulation of the loft. To their surprise, the workmen found a bomb wedged in the timbers in the roof space. The damage to his house had not been caused by blast but by impact from the bomb which had lain there undisturbed for 50 years!

It has to be remembered that Britain was effectively an armed fortress during the war. As well as the military training grounds, air force bombing ranges, ammunition stores all over the country, there were extensive areas of the coastline that were mined against enemy invasion. These factors plus the massive range of souvenirs will continue to employ experts for years to come. Some years ago the annual total of finds amounted to over 4,000, all potentially deadly.

In 1988 one of the home EOD units of the RAOC attended call outs for the following incidents:

Six Improvised Explosive Devices, four Explosive Devices, three Incendiaries and five Ammunition finds, 29 hoax and 121 false alarms; in addition 19 accidents, 231 ammunition or explosive failures and 12 incidents involving defects with ammunition or equipment.

Also, as part of their duties a total of 146 lectures were given to military, police and civilian personnel, and this was only one of the units on 24 hours a day, 365 days a year standby.

When attending an incident, the operator does do not know which category it is until he 'opens the box'. Adrenaline flows all the time until the climax or anticlimax point is reached.

Some readers might recall the very popular TV series, *Danger UXB,* which covered the work of the Royal Engineers during the early days of the Second World War. Following this series, those still involved in the clearance and disposal work, the Royal Engineers and the Royal Army Ordnance Corps, saw an increase in their work load. The viewer suddenly recognised Dad's little collection for what it really was, death and destruction on the sideboard!

A scrap dealer casually contacted the police; he had what appeared to be two shells amongst the rubbish in his yard at Sheffield. An inspection identified these as two 14-inch naval shells each weighing in at around one ton. These were not easy items to examine, especially when covered in rust but an X-ray quickly established what the contents were, and a crane helped shift them both to a more secure location. How they came to be there was never resolved. They may well have been war-time souvenirs!

Most of these highly trained specialists do not come into regular contact with some of the strange devices of the First and Second World Wars. Identification of some strange objects defeats them, but their problem can normally be solved by the Explosive Ordnance Disposal Technical Information Centre. (See Chapter 3.)

Disposal of wartime ordnance does not only result from public 'finds'. Over the past ten years, the Royal Engineers, in the form of 33 Engineer Regiment (EOD) and 101 Engineer Regiment (EOD) (V), have cleared more than 50 old airfields in the south of England. During the war when invasion seemed imminent pipe mines filled with explosive were laid under the airfields to ensure their destruction if Germany managed to invade. The most recent incident occurred in the early 1990s, when after some six months' planning and work a further fifteen charges were safely removed and destroyed. When explosives are stored under the most unsuitable conditions, the explosive content often breaks down and leaks out liquid nitroglycerine. This is fairly unstable at best; when liquid far more so and when in crystal form it is a case of 'sooner you than me'.

A Royal Engineers' bomb disposal team went to the rescue when Liverpool's Walton district ground to a halt after the discovery of a massive unexploded bomb. Roads were closed and dozens of homes were evacuated around Walton after workmen laying new sewers stumbled across a Second World War 500lb bomb buried 20 feet below ground.

The bomb in this case was identified by an operator from the Liverpool-based North West RAOC Explosive Ordnance Disposal Detachment who was the first expert on the scene. Operational procedures required the Royal Engineers to be called in because of their special expertise in wartime German aerial bombs. There was even a chance that the Saturday afternoon fixture at Everton Football Club would have to be postponed. But the Royal Engineers from 33 Engineer Regiment saved the day and managed to defuse the bomb after a 20-hour operation involving both the Army and the police.

Major Mike Lauder, who commanded the nine-man unit, said workmen who discovered the bomb had a narrow escape.

'Lying in the ground for around 40 years, the explosive and fusing mechanism had begun to deteriorate, and was not too stable,' he explained. 'But we eventually managed to flush the explosive out with water.'

The bomb's awkward position made the job even more hazardous than usual, he said. 'Heavy rain was washing away the sides of the trench where the device lay, threatening to dislodge it. We had to bring it gently to the surface to deal with it.'

A report of 1989 illustrates the extent of this work in the UK:

> Increased terrorist activity and a greater public awareness of security have led to a record number of call outs by Army bomb disposal experts. HQ of 11 Ordnance Battalion (EOD) responded to 1,030 calls in 1989; it also carried out a total of 4,005 conventional ammunition disposal tasks.

The work ranged from visiting scenes of explosions to offer expert advice and to clear secondary devices, to disposing of devices left by animal rights extremists. A disturbing aspect was the continuing number of young people injured in home-made bomb experiments. 11 Ordnance Battalion is on a national call out (with the exception of the area within the M25 boundary which is covered by the Metropolitan Police's own disposal squad); 85 per cent of the tasks are completed by the RAOC teams, with a contribution from the Royal Engineers, the Royal Air Force and the Royal Navy. A police amnesty in 1989 brought in mementoes from the Boer War to the Falklands which contributed to the increased work load.

Tailpiece

There are many incidents worthy of mention that have occurred on the British mainland over the years since the end of the war. It is only necessary to talk to an Ammunition Technical Officer and the anecdotes will be given, often with a wry smile.

There was the incident when a technician was asked if he could open the regimental safe, an old one for which no-one could find a key. Ever helpful, yes came the prompt reply. The safe was taken outside to a safe place, and the powers that be duly advised to expect a loud bang. Regrettably they were a little involved in more important matters and when the resultant bang came, they thought they had come under an IRA mortar attack. The ATO was suddenly faced by a squad of armed soldiers ready to defend their Colonel with their own lives.

In yet another incident, called out by armed police, they had found an IRA arms cache in a wood. The area was under close surveillance for a number of days when a man arrived with a shovel, dug up a bag and departed on his travels; he then threw the bag in a lake. Not to alarm the suspect he was followed home and a close watch was kept. The sack was retrieved from the lake and the ATO called in to examine the deadly contents. Yes, they were deadly, a dead cat to be precise. Not to be outdone and to retain an element of farce the wet sack complete with contents was quietly deposited on the suspect's doorstep and everyone went back home.

Another incident involved one of the better known cavalry regiments. A routine inspection of their ammunition found an unexpected and unacceptable quantity of ammunition that had obviously been misused and damaged. The ATO reported to the Adjutant on the result of his inspection and that regrettably they would be charged for the cost of the damaged ordnance. When dealing with aristocratic regiments the unusual has to be expected. The Adjutant casually asked what the cost was likely to be, and promptly got out a cheque book. Not the way the game is played old chap!

Finally, there was the story of a very young lieutenant, later to retire having served as a Brigadier and Director of Land Service Ammunition. Many years ago the Ordnance stores included two types of rockets, large and small. The large rockets had long wooden sticks, the small ones a shorter stick. Prior to the annual inspection this young officer, diligent to the extreme, checked his stock and found that there were far too many sticks for the large rocket, and too few for the smaller version. Having counted once, twice, three times and having his Sergeant check again, the only solution to getting the stocks right was to instruct his ever faithful Sergeant to get a saw, and correct the quantity of the sticks by type. The deed was done and the Sergeant was sworn to secrecy on pain of death.

The General duly arrived, was satisfied that all was in order and eventually left. There was then confusion and consternation when the Colonel turned to his young officer and softly enquired 'Have you any more of that firewood left'?

CHAPTER 7

NORTHERN IRELAND

321 EOD Unit

Although the IRA had been active in a somewhat sporadic way from 1956 it was not until 1969/70 that a serious campaign started; by April 1970 some 29 explosions had been investigated and three devices successfully dismantled. During April and October 1970 there had been 80 explosions and a total of 57 explosive and incendiary devices. Fortunately, in June 1969 321 EOD Unit had been established with a complement of ten ATOs and ATs, their initial role being to fly overseas at short notice to support any EOD threat that might arise. This far sighted action was to be of immense benefit to the security forces both at home and in Northern Ireland.

321 EOD sent its first section to Northern Ireland in May 1970 for a six-month period, comprising Captain R. N. Lennox, Sergeant W. Banfield and support staff. Although the individuals returned home, 321 EOD has been in Northern Ireland ever since.

The escalation of incidents of improvised explosive devices (IED) continued, the car bomb came into being, and anti-handling devices were added to the bombs. The original tour of duty in the Province for an AT was two years; this was very quickly reduced to four months, so great was the work load, working and living conditions and the strain of the job.

In the early days the death rate amongst both officers and men was very high, and came to be regarded as abnormal, unnecessary and unnerving: it was the subject of considerable discussion and change, as detailed in the section on Psychometric Testing.

Captain David Stewardson was the first fatality, at Castlerobin on 9 September 1971, whilst dealing with what turned out to be a device of novel design. WO2 Colin Davies died at Lurgan on 24 November, Staff Sergeant Chris Cracknell and Sergeant Anthony Butcher died in Belfast on 15 March 1972. Major Bernard Calladene was killed in Belfast 29 March, Captain John Young killed at Forkill on 15 July, WO2 William Clark killed at Clady on 18 August and Sergeant Roy Hill killed at Lurgan on 5 December 1972.

The supreme sacrifice made by these men was not in vain, as a great deal was learnt about the bombs and the bombers. Many of those who worked in the field survived and the information gathered added to the store to deal with future devices.

An EOD team consists of four soldiers who form a highly specialised and cohesive unit. The team leader, No. 1 operator, is the one who makes all the decisions and who walks forward to deal with the device. The No. 2 operates the Wheelbarrow robot and is experienced to assume the position of No. 1 in the event of a mishap. The No. 3 in the team is the signals and electronics expert, whilst No. 4 is an infantry soldier who acts as bodyguard for the team. In such a small unit, as well as the obvious need for a high level of specialist training, a very special personality is required, steady, conscientious people who remain cool despite all manner of distractions and dangers. The citations for the gallantry awards, from Savernake Forest in 1946 to Northern Ireland in 1994, demonstrate a similarity of characteristics of people working in this field.

It should be noted that the ATOs and ATs who form teams are more than adequately supported by other highly trained personnel. Signallers from the Royal Corps of Signals, drivers from the Royal Corps of Transport as well as the RAOC and RAOC specialists who operate the Wheelbarrow devices. The Royal Electrical and Mechanical Engineers provide service facilities for all the equipment in use.

One former senior officer, who served as a team leader in the early 1970s, reminisces 'Looking back to the early days, I suppose some people would have described us as a bit cavalier, going in with maybe only a flak jacket and a pair of running shoes'. The kit has changed dramatically but the people are still the same, so is the job which remains to safeguard lives and property.

Felix

During the early 1970s in Northern Ireland it became necessary to coin a call sign, when soldiers in the field needed the assistance of one of the RAOC bomb teams. There does not seem to be any individual who claims to be the originator, but the order 'Fetch Felix' was accepted as that call sign.

By the mid-1970s one AT based in Londonderry had become a proficient amateur cartoonist, spending his spare time illustrating incidents from the work in the province. Staff Sergeant Bryan Shepherd (later Major) was the creator of Felix the Cat, with nine or more lives, which is now the recognised badge of 321 EOD Company, and which adorns the special tie worn only by those members of the Corps who have 'tackled a live one'. Felix, complete with helmet and flak jacket, slightly scruffy and decidedly surprised, reflects those in the trade, their high morale, good humour and high degree of modesty.

Operations and Incidents

Over the years since 1970 the number of awards for gallantry to officers and men in the EOD units has been considerable. Never before in the history of the Royal Army Ordnance Corps has such a small band of people earned so many decorations. The list of those honoured is shown at the end of this book. Due to the security risk to those involved little real publicity is ever given to them. Only they and their colleagues really know what took place and with the true character of heroes they seldom speak out.

Regrettably, for the same security reasons it is not possible to deal with the detailed particulars of specific incidents, more especially those during recent years. However, some information has already been published in one source or another.

The 1970s saw an increase in the size and sophistication of the terrorist device. At the outset these were generally small with simple initiation systems; often a clothes peg was used as the trigger but later tilt and other switches were in use and then time devices followed. Sometimes devices had more than one method of initiation, and after a while booby-traps were fitted. There followed more sophisticated devices not targeted at a specific buildings but at the technicians they guessed would attend the incident. An added danger to the technicians was the use of snipers. If a device is in an exposed position the poor old AT can be a sitting duck.

The early devices would be up to ten pounds of explosive. Later these started to exceed one thousand pounds, and even though the majority would be one of the fertiliser-based home made explosives (HMX to the trade) the bang and resultant devastation would be considerable.

Again as the terrorists gained more experience so their tactics became better planned and more complex. The car bomb, first used by the IRA in 1971, became a usual means of delivery. However, the bombers and the delivery agents were not immune to self destruction, an event which became known as an 'own goal' in the trade. By 1973 some 61 had met the great bombers in the sky.

As well as straightforward explosive devices, blast incendiary bombs soon appeared. These created severe blast damage and splattered ignited petrol all around. A blaze of such ferocity followed that it was very hard for the fire brigade to really do much more than contain the fire from spreading to adjacent property.

The experiences of the 1970s resulted in the creation of a highly efficient unit within the British Army, probably the most skilled in the world. The relatively short tour of duty also meant that the core of highly trained technicians, both officers and men, continued to grow. 321 EOD Company expanded, from a small unit under the command of a major, as the size and responsibility increased, to that of a lieutenant colonel. As well as responsibility for incidents in Northern Ireland the battalion, as it became, maintains teams on the UK mainland, responsible for dealing with all incidents at home, apart from within the Metropolitan Police area which has its own disposal personnel. They are all skilled ex-Army technicians with active service experience. It is perhaps a result of the work in Northern Ireland that the differential between officers, warrant officers and Senior NCOs, and all those who deal with the devices has changed, all are now known as ATOs (Ammunition Technical Officers) whilst serving in the province.

The work of those from the camp at the 'sharp end' was recorded in the BBC TV film *The Bomb Disposal Men.* Filming took place on location and used real people, fortunately at a time when the workload had fallen during one of the truces that occurred from time to time.

Early recognition was given to the men of 321 EOD Company. In 1977 the Unit was awarded the Wilkinson Sword of Peace. In 1973 WO2 J. M. Coldrick, who was awarded the George Medal for a distinguished tour in the Province, was elected Army Man of the Year, receiving a presentation at a luncheon at the Savoy Hotel. Later as a captain he served a further tour and was awarded the MBE for Gallantry.

The following anecdotes are a sample of the many incidents recorded over the years, some serious some less so, the humour often only being apparent after the incident – and a cup of tea.

There was the lieutenant colonel who was on the roof of a bungalow fishing around in the chimney for a device. His team saw him gingerly extract a black object, carefully lay it on the lip of the chimney, then peer at it as if it had a most unpleasant smell. Suddenly he froze, then ignoring the ladder, plummeted down the tiles and crashed off the roof onto the ground; spectators said his legs were moving before he landed. 'The bloody clock has started to tick', was all he could say. His Warrant Officer casually recorded, 'Well at least we know why our nickname is Felix, a cat couldn't have come off that roof any faster.' The tension was eased by a good laugh all round. Shortly afterwards the colonel went back up and neutralised the bomb.

Another time the colonel arrived at the scene first and waited for the team to follow. The noisy approach of the pig, siren going, blue light flashing, all eyes now riveted on the vehicle, a short, stout corporal emerged, but no technician. The well meaning lad, one of the reserves, had acted on the call out, deciding to get the kit there and hope an AT would follow. The situation developed like a Whitehall farce; they couldn't find the key to the back of the vehicle, had problems operating the Wheelbarrow (these were a corporal clerk and a lieutenant colonel, probably both better suited to higher matters). Still they continued and help arrived in the form of an AT sergeant. Headquarters had forgotten to call him out when the operation started. Now with help, work started again, the Wheelbarrow got bogged down and the horrible nightmare continued. Eventually all was well and the device was disrupted. It proved to be a hoax. Neither the Colonel or the Corporal could have thought that it was very funny.

Even those innocents who are involved can act in some strange ways. There is the story of a van that was hijacked; the driver was told there was a bomb in the back, to drive it to the city centre and then abandon it. He had been sent on his way at 1.00pm. When questioned at 1.45pm and asked about the time delay, the driver advised that he had visited one or two customers on his way.

There was the incident of the officer who had to enter a roof space in a building by means of a small trap door. With a parka over his flak jacket he was a fairly bulky figure. After a struggle he got up and fitted a hook and line to the device but as he tried to go down he got stuck and his parka rose over his head. He then found the line, now attached to the

The IRA targets and terrorist incidents over the past twenty years on mainland UK include the following

Date	Place	Event
1972	Aldershot	Parachute Regiment HQ Bomb. 7 killed, 19 injured.
1974	London	Tower of London bomb. 1 killed, 38 injured.
1974	M62 Manchester	Bomb on bus, 12 killed, many injured.
1974	Guildford	Bomb in 2 pubs, 5 killed, 65 injured.
1974	Birmingham	Bombs in 2 town centre pubs, 19 killed, 120 injured.
1979	London	Conservative MP killed when bomb exploded under car (Airey Neave).
1981	London	Chelsea barracks, bomb attack, 2 killed, 37 injured.
1981	London	Oxford Street, 1 killed.
1982	London	Hyde Park & Regents Park, bombs, 11 soldiers killed, 51 injured.
1983	London	Harrods bomb, 6 killed, 91 injured.
1984	Brighton	Grand Hotel, bomb, 5 killed, 34 injured.
1988	Lockerbie	Flight Pan Am 103, bomb on plane, major damage on ground 270 dead, many injured.
1990	Deal	Bomb, 10 bandsmen killed.
1990	London	Bomb, Carlton Club, 20 injured.
1990	Eastbourne	Ian Gow killed by car bomb.
1991	London	Paddington & Victoria railway stations, 1 killed, 40 injured.
1991	St Albans	'Own goal', bombers killed while planting bomb.
1992	London	Baltic Exchange bomb, 3 killed, major property damage.
1993	London	Harrods bomb, 4 injured.
1993	London	High Street Camden, bomb, 18 injured.
1993	Warrington	Bombs in town centre, 2 children killed, many injured.
1993	London	Bishopsgate, lorry bomb, 1 killed, major property damage, many injured.
1994	London	Mortar attack, Heathrow Airport, no injuries, minor damage.
1996	London	Canary Wharf lorry bomb, major property damage, 2 killed.
1996	London	'Own goal', bomber killed on bus, Aldwych, London.
1996	Manchester	Arndale Centre, major property damage, 200 injured.

bomb, was also stuck; he could go neither up nor down. After a great deal of perspiration and contortion he extricated himself. It turned out to be a live device and he successfully neutralised it.

A certain warrant officer was called out to deal with a car bomb up an alley, alongside a paint store. A walk to recce the scene indicated that it was under the control of a sniper. The only way was to send in the Wheelbarrow to affix a tow rope. As a right angle was involved the rope had first to be passed round a lamp post. All was going well. The car was in the open and an explosive charge now had to be fixed to the Wheelbarrow to open it. Regrettably when the Wheelbarrow set off, the charge fell off and exploded. The AT was blown backwards and, when asked if he was all right, thought his Army career was over as he couldn't hear a word. However a trip to the hospital confirmed his deafness was only temporary, so he returned back to base. It was only when he stripped for a shower he realised that when the explosive charge had gone off he had been kneeling down and the front of his flak jacket had lifted up. He did not feel inclined to make a second visit to the hospital, so spent a considerable time with a pair of tweezers fishing bits of stone out of his stomach and legs.

An incident in the Province involved a football, kicked around a police post yard by soldiers and policemen for some three months. Every search dog that saw it rushed over barking and rolled it around. At the end of three months it was looking a little sad and one day it split open. 'Funny, it had always been heavy... perhaps, to help the dogs... what are those funny wires and ... isn't that very like Semtex? Call Felix!' The football had been filled with Semtex with a pendulum type firing mechanism, and then filled up with the sort of foam used to insulate cavity walls. It had been tossed over the wall in the hope that the first member of Manchester United who came along and kicked it would wonder at the roar of the crowd! Fortunately, the foam filling had gummed up the works. The moral of this story can safely be left to the reader.

One of the nerve-wracking aspects of the AT's job is the journey from base to the site of an incident. Most people can recall hair raising stories of frantic car rides. Those who work for the Metropolitan Police travel by Range Rover, driven by very experienced police drivers. Invariably a high speed drive through the thick traffic, with lights flashing and sirens howling, on the wrong side of the road. Many arrive at the incident in a state of shock. In Northern Ireland it can be difficult to build up to a terrifying speed in a heavy armoured vehicle, but a helicopter is a different matter. This is one job where speed is paramount and in the rural areas air transport is necessary, not only for the personnel, but also to transport the equipment needed to render a device safe. There have been many stories: one of the best concerns a pilot in the Army Air Corps who had apparently been an AT before he got his wings. When transporting an AT to a suspect car, he requested the landing location. The AT asked if he could be positioned behind the car, could he get a closer look – could they get a little lower as he couldn't quite see in the car's rear window. The pilot eventually offered to land his helicopter on the roof of the car, if this would help.

The pilot would have been grounded by his superiors, for such an apparent lack of care of his equipment, but his knowledge of the job in hand, his flying skill and his courage was of considerable help in dealing with a potentially dangerous situation as quickly as possible.

A question often asked is how do wives and families cope with the stress of not knowing what the AT will be doing, or whether they will be coming home. One WO2, who married late in life, never told his wife what his job really was. It was only on his return home one eventful day that he was met at the door by his distraught spouse, 'I know what you do!' she said. When asked how this could be, she admitted that she had seen him on the TV News on one of the rare occasions when an AT in full kit, but minus his helmet, appeared on TV.

A 30lb device had been discovered hidden in a pram which was being pushed through a residential area. To prevent damage to property the pram was moved to a stretch of waste ground. As this was before the days of robots and Pig Stick Disrupters, the device was dealt with by use of the trusty shot-gun. Unfortunately the detonator must have been hit, though the resolute No.1 never heard the actual explosion, only the echo as it reverberated away, sending shock waves all around. The No.1 lost his hearing for a couple of hours, and then continued with the job.

In order to convey to the reader the scale of activity in Northern Ireland the following table is based on official statistics, though this only lists the main types and annual totals it does indicate the numerical scale of the problem.

Terrorist Bomb Disposal Activity in Northern Ireland, 1971–1995

Improvised Explosive Devices vary from the small incendiaries designed for attacks on commercial property and under-car booby-traps, to huge car-borne bombs. Between these two extremes are a range of devices, for example, the Mark 15 Grenade ('Coffee Jar' bomb); the grenade launcher PRIG (Projected Recoilless Improvised Grenade) of 1991; the 1989 Mark 12 mortar, a horizontal tube which fires an anti-armour warhead, the improvised anti-armour grenade which is a hand-thrown device; the 1992 Mark 15 mortar, the 'Barrack Buster' used in over 50 attacks, containing a massive amount of explosive and producing a devastating effect. The Mark 16 mortar succeeded the Mark 12 in 1993 and has been used in 32 incidents.

Incidents dealt with by 321 EOD in Northern Ireland

Year	IED	Explosions	Incendiary	Total incidents
1971	508	1022	–	3403
1972	524	1409	–	5083
1973	555	1003	101	6786
1974	439	734	433	4797
1975	237	406	52	3134
1976	439	770	220	4153
1977	174	383	428	2843
1978	241	478	66	2647
1979	182	424	42	2086
1980	140	282	9	1604
1981	144	207	36	1972
1982	135	202	36	1707
1983	127	257	19	1570
1984	59	187	7	1255
1985	100	149	25	1232
1986	111	170	16	1257
1987	188	229	15	1839
1988	235	246	13	1825
1989	218	240	14	1980
1990	158	181	17	2509
1991	253	240	134	2649
1992	215	221	72	2509
1993	92	192	27	948
1994	140	119	36	1134
1995	20	2	1	176

In 1991 the largest home made explosive device thus far was encountered, 3,500kg (around 7,700lb). It was successfully neutralised. That year also saw a significant increase in the use of projected recoilless improvised grenades. 1992 reports show that during the past twenty years 321 EOD Company has dealt with more than 40,000 emergency calls of one sort or another, involving over 700,000 pounds of explosives. Seventeen EOD operators have been killed on duty together with three team members; and 22 have been injured.

As recorded, awards for gallantry in Northern Ireland include three George Crosses, 35 George Medals, 21 OBEs, 30 MBEs, 18 BEMs and 69 QGMs.

A note from *Hansard* in 1981 records that the Under Secretary for Defence, Philip Goodhart, reported to the House of Commons:

> Of all the invaluable work performed by the Armed Forces in the Province, few tasks are so consistently demanding and dangerous as the work of the RAOC bomb disposal teams. Their levels of technical skill, coupled with ice cool nerves, commanded the highest admiration and respect even among other members of the security forces in the Province, who themselves face the dangers of terrorist attack. Men with the necessary attributes are a rare commodity, and at any one time there are only about fifty of them in small teams throughout the Province.

CHAPTER 8

THE FALKLANDS (1982) AND THE GULF (1990–1991)

The Falklands: Recollections of ATs

The clear up after the surrender was a mammoth task. Large quantities of ammunition, ranging from Exocet missiles down to rifle and pistol ammunition, were dumped all over the islands in every conceivable type of location. At the start there was a joint EOD centre, RAOC and Royal Engineers, and the RAOC technical staff were quickly reinforced by four ATs flown in from the UK. However, it soon became apparent that this unit was still inadequate to deal with the magnitude of the task.

Perhaps to indicate more clearly what was involved, the Argentinian ammunition had been supplied by a variety of other countries, Italy, Spain, USA, UK, France, Israel and even the USSR. As in any field of conflict the positions that had been defended were full of ready-to-use ammunition, artillery, mortar, rocket and guided missiles. In many locations this was made more difficult because the defence positions had been destroyed by our own barrages and as a result the ready-for-use ammunition was scattered over a wide area and was in a damaged and dangerous condition. The island racecourse illustrated a particular problem. The Argentinians had dug large, deep pits, filled them with ammunition and covered them with camouflage, but when the thaw set in the pits rapidly filled with water.

The solution to the complex problem was to form a composite ammunition company and to send it to the islands as quickly as possible. The company was duly formed in July 1982. Sixty personnel in total from the RAOC and Royal Pioneer Corps all assembled at the RAOC training depot, at Deepcut.

As will be appreciated, there was a great deal of excitement at the thought of the task in hand, and a degree of trepidation as to what might be found when work started. The Army, in its usual fashion, tried to consider all possible problems; for example, toothache. When the nearest dentist was in Buenos Aires, a dental check was vital. (My father along with most of his regiment had all of his teeth removed before going to the front in the First World War.) Thankfully, such a drastic step was not considered necessary in this later conflict.

The Commanding Officer of the company, Major Peter Courtney-Green, decided that his troops needed to 'wear in' the new Combat Boots, High, prior to leaving the UK. The company had to gallop about in these during five-mile 'bashes'. Though it did not ensure fitness in all, it caused problems in the feet of many. Despite the trials and tribulations spirits were generally very high. A worthwhile job had to be carried out, not only to clear up and dispose of the damaged and unserviceable ammunition but also to create a viable stock of serviceable ammunition throughout the islands, for use against any future attack by the Argentinian forces.

The advance party under the command of Warrant Officer (Conductor) Steve Harmon, set off for the Falklands in late July. The first stop was Dacca, Senegal. On landing the plane was surrounded by armed Senegalese troops and the party was ordered not to leave the vicinity of the aircraft. Those present were not sure whether the soldiers were protecting the party or stopping an invasion of their country by the RAOC. Next stop was Ascension Island. Early in the morning the troops embarked there on to a Hercules so as to arrive in Stanley during daylight. The first problem occurred when the pilot could not start the engines and everyone had to get into another aircraft. This one managed to get airborne and breakfast was served. After twenty minutes this aircraft developed a fault and had to return to Ascension. No further aircraft was available so during a short 24-hour break, soldiers relaxed in the sun. The next day all went well and the fourteen-hour flight to Stanley was completed without further problems. There was in-flight refuelling which was fascinating to watch; if there had been any problem with this then it would have been a case of 'Montevideo here we come!'

Though Stanley was what had been expected, the cold, wet wind and the chaos still came as a shock. Geof Cox, a member of the main task force, had arranged for the party to be accommodated in a house, supposedly more comfortable than a tent. It had no hot water, a peat stove that could not be used and a bath better suited to curing sheep-skins, but with a magnificent view over Stanley harbour.

The first day was spent meeting the ATOs and ATs of 421 EOD Company who had been with the Task Force throughout the campaign.

Dick Gill, Kevin Callaghan, Johno Johnson and Geof Cox had already started the clearance of Stanley and very quickly filled the new arrivals in on what to expect.

The remainder of the company arrived a few days later. There were six months to complete the task, the major objectives of which were:

1 Clearance of all unexploded ordnance throughout the Falkland Islands and South Georgia.
2 Sorting into categories: serviceable, repairable or for disposal.
3 Establishing a field storage ammunition depot in Stanley.
4 Calculating the theatre requirement for ammunition, both for operations and training.
5 Deploying operational stocks to forward positions throughout the islands.
6 Establishing an inspectorate and ammunition branch at the headquarters.
7 Supporting units for exercises and firings.
8 Conducting surveillance of ammunition performance during training for the UK headquarters.

Sergeant Jack Horner had control of one of the larger holding areas for all ammunition and explosives collected up from around Stanley. This was an Aladdin's cave containing everything from Exocet missiles to rifle ammunition. It was a magnificent display which Jack took great delight in showing and describing in great detail to anyone who called by, from the Quartermaster General to media personnel and visiting politicians.

Teams were deployed around the islands to get the job underway. Apart from the expected problems of ammunition in a ready-for-use condition and the identification of other nations' supplies, the generally poor quality of the individual packaging and its inability to withstand the harsh environment all helped to make the job more difficult. The Falklands' weather also caused problems, some of the ammunition was by now resting under some ten feet of snow, and some areas had to be visited on more than one occasion.

The bulk of the clearance work was around Stanley itself. There were at least 40 known sites that had to be dealt with. The high ground that had been the scene of such bitter fighting had to be tackled. Every possible type of transport was used including vehicles which had previously belonged to the Argentinians. There were also the sad and traumatic occasions when the bodies of the victims of the conflict were found among the ammunition.

The safe but disposable ammunition had to be blown up. A demolition area was established about three miles from Stanley and a team of three ATs and six Pioneers lived and worked there in dreadful conditions, completing about six 'blows' a day, each of about two tons. The demolition ground consisted of the usual splinter-proof shelter, constructed out of stone-filled ammunition boxes with electrical initiation cables running for half a mile to the pits. The ammunition awaiting disposal was held in areas back along the road to Stanley, each containing around 30 tons. The nearest was some 60 metres away from the actual demolition ground which was located in a natural depression in the ground.

Preparing the second blow of the day Ron Stafford carried out all of his safety checks, including looking for wandering helicopters which had a fascination for trying to find out what was going on, and retired to the comfort of his splinter-proof shelter. He initiated his firing unit. He felt the planned detonation go off satisfactorily, closely followed by a somewhat larger bang. Ron waited a bit for the effects to die down but, when they did not, decided to see what had gone wrong. The entire first holding area had gone off, so there was little alternative but to try and stage the Falklands Olympics, bad back and all; and, in the best tradition of the ATs of old, he rapidly departed the scene. The cause of this unplanned event was never discovered. However, the resultant crater confirmed that all 30 tons had gone off. Whilst it was estimated that this cut down the usual tidying up stage by about three weeks, it was considered prudent to move back the holding areas to about a kilometre from the demolition area. Thankfully for all concerned, higher authority accepted that the accident was unfortunate, and left it at that.

The storage pits at the racecourse presented a difficult task. Not only was the ammunition well under water and below the water table, but there was a deadline for completion to enable the annual Stanley races to take place. The Corps always did have a strong sense of priorities.

The clearance work progressed and an ammunition depot was established including a processing building. Items were sorted and passed back for training use by the troops. Operational stocks were shipped around the island by means of LSL *Sir Bedivere* and the defensive positions resupplied in quantity. The company had arrived in July for a six-month tour. They spent Christmas on the islands in the true and traditional way of the British Army. One novelty was being allowed a three-minute telephone call home, to their loved ones. It is not easy to whisper words of endearment when someone is standing alongside with a stopwatch!

By the end of the tour it was estimated that some 3,500 tons of ammunition had been recovered for future use in the Falklands, some 2,500 tons had been returned to the UK for either disposal or future use and around 1,000 tons had been demolished locally.

January 1983 saw the cruise home; ten days on the *Cunard Countess* to Ascension, then a plane to Brize Norton to a VIP welcome. The Director General Ordnance Services, Director Land Service Ammunition and the Corps Band were joined by the most important people – the servicemen's wives, parents and children.

[*Author's note*: I am greatly indebted to Steve Harmon for his recollection of this period of his service life.]

The Gulf War 1990–1991: Recollections of ATs

The Gulf War was another in the long series of incidents in which the RAOC ammunition technicians, both commissioned and other rank, were involved. October 1990 saw the arrival of ammunition technicians from 421 Company based in Germany, together with other members of 11 EOD Battalion RAOC. The AT personnel consisted of a Major, three Warrant Officers class 1, two Warrant Officers class 2, four Staff Sergeants, one Sergeant and three Corporals, sufficient to form four separate EOD/IED teams, if required. The personnel included a specialist in chemical and biological ordnance who had previously been an instructor in this field at the School of Ammunition.

This strange group were initially quartered in camps that had been provided by the local government to accommodate pilgrims on the long trek to Mecca. Though this was not the norm for such an elite group, with the undisputed skill of the AT they soon made themselves reasonably comfortable.

As the reader will be aware, this was the period before the true conflict started. There was no need to worry about terrorist activity in the neighbourhood of Riyadh as the local security forces had long ago rounded up all likely suspects. The main task involved the control of live firing ranges for the troops. It has to be remembered that 'peace-time' soldiers do not get a lot of experience with live ammunition and it was essential to rectify this as quickly as possible. Hence, the latter part of 1990 saw the building of temporary ranges in the desert, and their constant use by all the coalition forces, which produced the usual catalogue of incidents.

The use of live hand grenades caused some problems in the desert sand. At times the grenades fell rather short and the ratchet mechanism had not fully functioned, being held back by the odd grain of sand. The disposal problem was made worse by the fact that walking up to the grenade could cause the sand to shift sufficiently to enable the grenade to fire, leaving the AT Range Officer with 3.4 seconds in which to leave the scene. Many infantry soldiers marvelled at the ability to move from a standing start to full gallop and travel a hundred yards in this remarkably short space of time!

One young soldier, when throwing his grenade (normally done in the manner of bowling at cricket) managed to swing his arm right round his body and drop the grenade just behind himself. By some miracle of God when it exploded he was not blown to bits. However, he lay there and screamed. The consternation can be appreciated. Up ran the medics, 'Where have you been hit?' 'My leg,' groaned the soldier. The medics looked but could see no blood. 'My calf at the back.' They cut open his trousers and after close examination found a spot the size of a pimple. The lucky lad had only been hit by a miniscule fragment. In the best spirit of the service and to bring back his confidence his platoon commander kindly provided a complete box of grenades, and made him use the lot.

A newspaper in the UK published a recipe for a cake, supposedly enjoyed by General Sir Peter de la Billière, commander of the British forces in the Gulf. The paper also provided Sir Peter's address to enable mothers, wives and girlfriends to send their offerings. The logistical problem this produced for the ATs, having to examine thousands of parcels in case they contained an explosive device, can be imagined. The cakes were collected daily, transported to the British Embassy, X-rayed and brought back, before being distributed to the forces.

There was one incident that involved a Scud missile. Like most projectiles the Scud has a certain maximum range; in order to increase the range the Iraqi experts increased the fuel capacity and reduced the explosive content. As most children know, messing about with weight distribution, especially in an airborne object, tends to alter the flight stability. So it was with many Scuds. Most broke into three parts when they reached Riyadh and it was the warhead section of one of these that the squad were tasked to deal with. Apart from bouncing over a six-lane highway and coming to rest by a petrol filling station, the greatest concern was that it ended up against the wall of a mosque. This meant it had to be disposed of. When the UK team arrived at the scene the Saudi, French and USA EOD teams were already on site, around 30 souls crowded round to offer advice. No evacuation had taken place and the location was totally out of control. To make matters worse the French experts had already cut a hole in the case with a hacksaw and were scooping out the explosive with a spoon – nouveau cuisine par excellence! The WO2 very quickly took charge, cleared the area of unwanted bodies, defuzed the missile and made it safe. Perhaps the other servicemen should have followed his example prior to leaving home – read up on what they might expect to come across, and be prepared for most eventualities.

At the end of any conflict comes the task of returning unused stores back to the home depot, a relatively simple one if they are contained in boxes and neat stacks. Regrettably, a lot of users 'up at the sharp end' do get carried away in the heat of battle and open boxes, load guns, arm grenades and effect similar unnecessary acts designed to make life troublesome for the RAOC. In this case, some even had the audacity to let their tanks get destroyed by the enemy, some were so slack that they let their bombs and shells land on neat stacks of enemy ammunition.

One of the tasks was to recover ready-for-use ammunition, ensuring that it was safe and in good condition, repacking and then shipping. Another was to dispose of the items that had been damaged, either by controlled explosions or dumping at sea. Abnormal climatic conditions can also have an adverse effect on normally stable stores. In the Gulf temperatures can rise to over 50° centigrade and in one instance a quantity of phosphorus stores caught fire spontaneously. Another involved an American vehicle depot where an armed vehicle exploded causing considerable damage and injury to the personnel in the vicinity.

The experience obtained in the Falklands proved of great value. In the Gulf it was a similar task involving the delivery of vast quantities of ammunition and then collecting it all together after the conflict, for return to base, after having disposed of the rubbish.

This interesting collection of issued documents relates to the Falklands War. I believe that it could just as easily relate to the Gulf, or Bosnia, or to any other war zone.

FALKLAND ISLANDS LOGISTIC BATTALION
EQUIPMENT / CLOTHING PACKING ORDER

1. Dress
Beret
Combat Jacket (top left pocket ID card, top right ear defenders)
Combat Trousers
Shirts Combat
Boots Combat
Socks Woollen
Jerseys Heavy Wool (when ordered)
Face Veil (to be worn around neck)
Gloves Combat (when ordered)
Webbing 58 Pattern
ID Discs (to be worn around neck)

2. Equipment and clothing is to be packed in the following manner:
a. Pouch Rear Left
  1 x Towel
  Washing Kit Personal
  1 x Set Mess Tins
  1 x KFS
Right – Cleaning Brushes & Polish
  Housewife
  1 x Pair Socks
  1 x Pair Underpants
  1 x Vest
  1 x Spare Laces
  10 metres String Green
  1 x Tin Foot Powder
b. Yoke – Field Dressing (taped to left hand side)
c. Carrier Cape – 1 x NBC Smock Protective (NBC Gloves inner/outer in chest pocket)
1 x NBC Trousers Protective
d. Respirator Case – Respirator with Canister Anti-Dim
  Decontamination Kit Personal No 1 Mk 1
  Decontamination Kit Personal No 2 Mk 1 (Puffer Bottle)
  Detector Paper No 1 Mk 2
  Detector Paper No 2 Mk 2
e. Pouch Ammunition Left – Ammo Magazines
f. Pouch Ammunition Right – Weapon Cleaning Kit
g. Holster (for 9mm Pistol)
  Lanyard
  Magazine
  Rod Cleaning
  Bottle Oil
h. Carrier Water – Water Bottle/Mug
j. Large Pack – 1 x Combat Jacket
  1 x Combat Trousers
  1 x Combat Liner
  1 x Combat Hood
  1 x Jersey Heavy Wool
  1 x Shirt Combat
  1 x Pants Thermal
  2 x Underpants Long
  2 x Underpants
  2 x Vests
  1 x Socks Woollen
  1 x Socks Arctic
  1 x Vest PT
  1 x Shorts PT
  1 x Shoes PT

1 x Combat Gloves (if not worn)
1 x Cap Comforter
1 x Sleeping Bag/liner (attached to top of pack with utility straps)
1 x 24 Hour Ration Pack (two side pockets of pack)

k. Kit Bag No.1 – 1 x Boots DMS
1 x Pair Puttees
1 x Boots NBC
1 x Boots Knee Rubber
1 x Foul Weather Smock
1 x Foul Weather Trousers
1 x Foul Weather Gloves Outer
1 x Foul Weather Gloves inner
2 x Socks Arctic
1 x Socks Sea Boot
1 x Headover
1 x Cap Arctic
1 x Vest Thermal
1 x Pants Thermal
1 x Jersey Heavy Wool (if not worn)
2 x Trousers Light Weight
1 x Towel
1 x Shirt Combat
1 x Vest PT
1 x Shorts PT
1 x Socks Woollen

l. Kit Bag No 2 – 1 x Parka DPM
1 x Liner Parka
1 x Bedroll
1 x Steel Helmet

Top up this bag with personal clothing / effects as required)

SATO FALKLAND ISLANDS
TECHNICAL AMMUNITION CIRCULAR No 1

Clearance of Ammunition and Explosives – Falkland Islands

1. The task of clearing the debris of war and in particular ammunition and explosives is potentially very hazardous whether it be British or Argentinean. There are a number of obvious and not so obvious reasons for assessing the situation as such and below are listed the circumstances under which ammunition may be found in anything but good condition.

a. The ammunition may have been prepared ready for firing, throwing, launching, etc., fuze caps removed on MOR/ARTY/RCL ammunition, MOR/ARTY/RCL primers, igniters exposed, grenades primed, demolition charges prepared, mines fuzed, rockets armed, weapons loaded.

b. The ammunition may have been removed from its primary and secondary pack thus exposing primers, fuzes, detonators, etc. and will probably be lying in positions where handling may be difficult (i.e. at the bottom of a 10 feet water hole).

c. It is possible that the area in which the ammunition is found is booby trapped or mined and may need RE search teams to be tasked for clearance.

d. Some Argentinean ammunition may have a design weakness which in itself renders the ammunition inherently unsafe, i.e. 105mm RCL ammo).

e. Past history of handling ammunition found is likely to be unknown and although visually it may look safe there is no knowing the internal condition of initiating mechanisms as a result of bad handling.

f. Description of ammo types in Spanish could lead to misinterpretation of method of use/type of round, etc. (i.e. chemical, WP matures).

g. The appearance of an item may be misleading as to its function or operation and effect (i.e. flash and sound unit).

h. Ammunition may be mixed in the same site in an incompatible arrangement.

2. Because of the points listed above it is necessary to introduce a number of safeguards that must be observed if both the public and military personnel are to be protected.

a. When clearance of an area is to be undertaken the team leader is to be an AT not below the rank of SGT.

b. All members of the team are to be properly briefed by the team leader before any task is undertaken. This briefing should include all the points listed in para 1a–g.

c. Before any clearance is started the team leader is to recce the area first to familiarise himself with the sort of task that lies ahead. He may need special equipment such as pumps/CGR, etc., in order to carry out the task. By doing the recce he will be better able to plan the task.

d. Before an area is cleared, confirmation as to whether J SEODRC have declared the area clear of booby traps or mines is to be obtained.

e. The dumps at Moody Brook and Airport Rd are to be under the control of a SGT AT until such time as all exposed ammunition is cleared away.

f. Any ammunition found which has any of its safety arrangements removed, damaged or disturbed is to be treated with extreme caution and action taken to protect/cover/replace the missing components where possible. If this cannot be achieved then SATO/ATO/SAT is to be contacted before the ammunition is moved.

g. The discovery of a type of ammunition that is not known or held as part of the display at Airport Rd dump is to be reported immediately to SATO/ATO/SAT. If the AT is uncertain as to the method of functioning, or role of any ammo then once again SATO/ATO/SAT is to be notified before the ammunition is moved.

h. The team leader is to familiarise himself with all the ammunition he is likely to encounter and have a working knowledge of its method of functioning, safety arrangements, intended effect, etc.

j. Ammunition is not to be moved without being held in at least its secondary pack. Where re-packing is not possible SATO/ATO/SAT authority is to be sought before transporting such ammunition by road.

k. Ammunition is only to be destroyed at the Demolition Ground Darwin Rd or in areas so designated by SATO. If the need arises to destroy ammunition outside of any of those areas then SATO/ATO/SAT authority is to be sought.

l. Vehicle commanders are to ensure that vehicles are loaded safely and that drivers observe all traffic regulations with due regard to condition of roads, and the nature of cargo.

m. Regardless of its apparent condition ammunition boxed or otherwise is not to be roughly handled.

n. Safety precautions concerning EED (in particular RF hazards + Anti Static) are to be observed.
(Signed)
P.B. Courtney-Green Maj. SATO FI

CHAPTER 9

SELECTION AND PROMOTION

Prospects for All

For those who undertook their basic training at Blackdown perhaps the following short poem, dated 1916, but author anonymous, remains as true now as it was then.

BLACKDOWN CAMP

There's an isolated, desolated spot I'd like to mention,
Where all you hear is 'Stand at Ease,' 'Slope Arms.'
'Quick March,' 'Attention'.
It's miles away from anywhere by Gad it is a rum'un.
A chap lived there for fifty years and never saw a woman.
There are lots of little huts, all dotted here and there.
For those who have to live inside I've offered many a prayer.
Inside the huts there's **rats** as big as any nanny goat.
Last night a soldier saw one trying on his overcoat.
It's sludge up to the eyebrows, you get it in your ears.
But into it you've got to go, without a sign of fear.
And when you've had a bath of sludge, you just set to and groom.
And get cleaned up for next parade, or else its 'Orderly Room'.
Week in, week out, from morn till night, with full pack and a rifle.
Like Jack and Jill, you climb the hills, of course that's just a trifle.
'Slope Arms', 'Fix Bayonets', then 'Present', they fairly put you through it.
And as you stagger to your hut, the Sergeant shouts 'Jump to it'.
With tunics, boots, and puttees off, you quickly get the habit.
You gallop up and down the hills just like a blooming rabbit.
'Heads backwards bend', 'Arms upward stretch', 'Heels raise', then 'Ranks change places'.
And later on they make you put your kneecaps where your face is.
Now when this War is over and we've captured Kaiser Billy
To shoot him would be merciful and absolutely silly;

Just send him down to Blackdown there among the rats and clay.
And I'll bet he won't be long before he droops and fades away.
– *but we're not downhearted yet!*

The selection and training of potential Ammunition Technicians has always been hard. The length of the course at the Ammunition School and its technical content is in reality rather like a short university course. Many have compared the training to that of a specialised Bachelor of Science degree. The educational standards of entrants has always been high, one instructor at the Ammunition School recalls teaching basic chemistry to a course on which seven national servicemen actually held degrees.

An AT is looked upon as a high calibre person; many are officer quality material who have elected to serve in the ranks. Many, and far more than in other arms of the services, progress through the ranks to become officers. In the old days these were classed as Quartermaster commissions. These then became Ammunition Executive Officer commissions. Latterly they are classified as Regular Officers (late entry). There is still the differentiation between those who joined in the ranks and those who passed through Sandhurst. Times are changing!

The present methods of selection start when a soldier expresses a wish to become an ammunition technician. A short one-week induction course and a series of tests usually lead to a 50 per cent rejection rate. If selected and having passed the psychometric tests without further rejections a candidate then starts a course at the School of Ammunition lasting some six months, which includes a period at the Royal Military College of Science, Shrivenham. Those who are fortunate to complete this intensive and demanding course then qualify as Class 2 tradesmen, and are promoted to the illustrious rank of lance corporal with a probationary period before promotion to corporal.

Approximately three years after leaving the school a technician then returns to undertake a further three-month extensive and specialised period of training to cover the aspects of the trade that are only permitted to be undertaken by a Class 1 tradesman. Since 1988 there are three such courses a year, limited to a maximum of sixteen students on each. In the 1950s the Class 1 qualification brought automatic promotion to the substantive rank of sergeant, the rank being held regardless of appointment. These days a Class 1 tradesman remains in the rank of corporal until he starts to prove his worth as a non-commissioned officer and gains the necessary experience. By this time he will have received the basic training in dealing with Improvised Explosive Devices, but is not qualified to go it alone. He would be a No. 2 in the team.

Prior to a posting to Northern Ireland he will attend another short, two- to three-week, course at the school to receive intensive training in IEDD and only if he passes this course will he go 'active'. There is no compulsion for an Ammunition Technician to serve in Northern Ireland or on any other IEDD work. However if he refuses a posting he would have to accept automatic regrading out of this trade to become a clerk, storeman or driver. Sooner than face the criticism of his peers under these circumstances, most choose to leave the Army .

For further promotion, as in all occupations, service and civilian, it is not enough to be qualified. An individual must gain experience, there must be an opening for advancement and there is an element of luck, being in the right place at the right time and being known and respected by the right people. All these are to a degree important. On the assumption than an individual knows what he wants and is educationally and psychometrically acceptable, then after joining the RAOC, he could expect to be a corporal Class 1 tradesman within five years. This might seem a long time, but it is necessary to train and develop an individual to the required standards both technically and mentally to enable him to perform his required duties in a safe and efficient manner. In the days of national service the same qualification and rank could be achieved in a much shorter time. The author joined on 1 October 1951 and was a Class 1 tradesman in the substantive rank of sergeant on 5 May 1953 and doubts if he was anywhere near as well suited for the rank as the present tradesmen.

A number of other examples of achievement show how some of the older hands progressed.

A Sergeant AT Class 1 in 1956 served as the Director Land Service Ammunition, a Brigadier, in 1989 and it is said he had to be persuaded to take a commission. A considerable number have progressed through the ranks to retire as lieutenant colonels and many have reached the rank of major. Some of the author's contemporaries from the 1950s still served the RAOC in positions as retired officers in the 1990s – a lifetime in ammunition.

In the 1950s a soldier could expect to reach the rank of sergeant in a couple of years, then have probably three years as sergeant, five years as staff sergeant, five years as a warrant officer class 2, three years as a warrant officer class 1 (sub conductor) and a further three years as a warrant officer class 1 (conductor), which is the highest non-commissioned rank in the British Army, senior to all regimental sergeant majors, even the Academy Sergeant Major at Sandhurst.

An example is one particular soldier who joined in 1951. He became a sergeant in November 1952, served four years as sergeant, six years as staff sergeant, five years as a WO2, two years as WO1 and five years in the ultimate rank of conductor; he was then commissioned and served one year as a lieutenant, nine years as a captain and five years as a major, retiring to join the staff as a retired officer.

So with a reasonable amount of luck it should be possible for a man to join at 18 and progress to become a warrant officer class 1 by his early 30s.

The reprint of a seniority roll in Chapter 3 indicates how a soldier could follow his progress. The course he was on was an indication to him of his seniority. The date shown was the date he qualified as a Class 1 tradesman, the '1st' or 'Ex' indicated exempt from, or the grade of Army Certificate of Education, the final date was his date of birth.

Those selected for the trade cost the Government around £20,000 to train to Class 2 and a further £10,000 to Class 1, at 1989 rates and are worth every penny.

An AT must now serve in a base type unit in the UK or Germany for approximately six months; after this period he can then be posted anywhere, Canada, Belize, Hong Kong, Cyprus, Falklands or Northern Ireland (these latter two as four-month tours of duty). If perhaps one of the lucky ones he could be posted to serve a two-year tour with the forces of another country, Canada, Borneo, Oman, Kuwait or the United Arab Emirates.

Regrettably, there is a fairly high rate of 'early retirement' within the trade, not only from the ranks, sergeants, staff sergeants and WO2s but also amongst the captains and young majors, people with over ten years' service. Times change and the Army has changed considerably over the past three decades; efficiency, improvements, cost control, the decline of the British Empire and frequent government political cut backs all tend to restrict promotion and pay. For these highly skilled and sought-after middle managers the prospects in Civvy Street are considerable. Some leave and become police constables where the pay is better than for a staff sergeant and overtime is available. Although the Merseyside Police Force does not have its own bomb squad it does have at least one ammunition technician on its strength who has experience in Northern Ireland.

CHAPTER 10

PSYCHOMETRIC TESTING

For many centuries there have been elite bodies, particularly within the services and in the warrior classes. For example, selection by height and strength brings to mind the royal guards within the Zulu tribes; also the Brigade of Guards in pre-war times, and Napoleon's personal guards renowned for their battle experience, height and whiskers. Not so long ago officers in the British Army were selected on the basis of their correct family and social background together with financial means.

Perhaps the Germans were the forerunners of the present system. During the First World War simple vocational selection was introduced and by 1939 the German services employed some 200 psychologists for the selection of officers and certain specialist groups. During the Second World War the British Army established a Directorate of Personnel Selection, introducing intelligence tests at recruiting centres and a general service scheme to allocate recruits. Many readers will recall the basic tests that national servicemen were subjected to. One of the early benefits of this innovation was an improvement at officer cadet selection and training. It was the result of the psychiatrists' input that the task and leaderless group situations were introduced, such as how to get an oil drum over a pit with a piece of string, a plank and ten men. Thank the Lord a lot has improved since this early start.

The most intensive testing of this kind ever developed was by the Americans for the selection of astronauts. The applicant has to undergo some 30 hours of psychiatric and psychological interview tests and stress situations and over 100 performance variables are correlated to produce the final grading. The purpose of these tests is to 'identify evidence of ability to respond predictably to foreseeable situations, without losing the capacity to adapt flexibly to circumstances which cannot be foreseen', an aim that could be applied to a very considerable number of occupations, including bomb disposal operators.

So far as the Ammunition Branch of the RAOC is concerned, apart from the very basic and primitive recruit testing, the present psychometric testing only started in the early 1970s. It very quickly became evident in 1971 and 1972 that the death rate among RAOC operators in Northern Ireland was far greater than expected. As a standard procedure, every incident which involved the death of the operator was closely investigated. Five operators were killed during a six-month period and the enquiries concluded that basic safety had been largely ignored; unaccountable human error was clearly an important cause and the Psychiatric Branch were consulted and a selection programme was eventually devised.

To put the risk into perspective, by 1975 the chance of an operator being killed was 50 times greater than for other soldiers in Northern Ireland. What was required of an operator during this period? He must complete a four-month tour of duty with a single mid-tour break. He must be technically competent and able to command total authority at an incident. As the man in charge he must be capable of resisting pressure from superiors with differing views on operational priorities. He is in the limelight and a potential target for snipers and hostile crowds. Add to these requirements the fact that he might be called to over 20 tasks within a 24-hour period, of which a high number could involve live devices. By 1975 an operator knew that one in every 23 had been killed. The job was dangerous and when making a manual approach he was not able to disperse the tension or fear by physical action in the same way as his infantry colleague in a riot or street incident.

The early psychiatric categories allocated to bomb disposal operators following selection were as follows:

Category A No reservations, should make an entirely satisfactory operator.

Category B+ Should make a satisfactory operator, some minor reservations which may require special observation or management during training or on tour.

Category B– Considerable doubt as to whether he will make a safe or suitable operator, significant reservations which indicate the need for careful investigations or reassessment of suitability by his branch.

Category C Considered unsuitable as an operator, important flaws in personality.

The question that faced the psychiatrist now was to evaluate personal qualities required by an operator. Four main characteristics were subdivided into fifteen sections:

Judgement: grasp, foresight, discrimination and evaluation.

Reliability: safety sense, mental approach, common sense and learning ability.

Flexibility: modification, concentration, self confidence and control.

Temperament: calmness, leadership and communication.

It was therefore no easy task for those responsible for deciding whom to select. In the very early days those involved in this procedure were more used to helping their patients get well and tended to give the candidate the benefit of any doubt. This was very much a major problem in the mid 1970s. At that time operators were tested just before their special training prior to an operational tour of duty in Northern Ireland. A soldier could have been a senior NCO and 'in the trade' for ten to fifteen years or more. If he failed the tests and was rejected for operational duty it could be the end of his career. Not many could face the stigma, real or imagined, of being regraded into another trade. This dilemma faced both the tester and candidate and it took several years before the system adjusted to the real problem.

There were three psychiatric tests used in the early days, giving a broad and overlapping picture of the subject's intelligence, attitudes, personality structure and psychological stability. The tests were the Clinical Analysis Questionnaire (CAQ), the Sixteen Personality Factor Questionnaire (16PFQ) and the Dynamic Personality Inventory (DPI). Even today these are very widely used and standardised tests of proven reliability. They are used not only to select various specialised groups in the Army but are also used in civilian life by some of the international personnel selection companies. None of the tests have a right or wrong answer and the subject is asked to agree or disagree with a particular statement, or to state if it is true or false. For example:

I am happiest alone, away from people.

I feel worn out and can't get enough rest.

I worry and think a lot about things that may go wrong.

I find it hard to address a large group.

Within all these tests there are built-in correlations which show up the subject who is giving the answers that he believes are those expected.

One problem often encountered is a subject who studies the question and tries to evaluate what his answer really is. Those above would be simple to respond to, less so the following:

If I had to choose I would rather be :

a) A forester.

b) Uncertain.

c) A secondary school teacher.

[*Author's note:* Frankly, for myself, I don't fancy either a), b) or c) and yet I am not uncertain.]

Another awkward question is: do you enjoy reading about sex? To which one candidate replied in more detail than usual 'only when I can't get the real thing,' which may have given a clear indication of his true character but created doubts as to his suitability!

Having completed the written tests each subject was interviewed by a psychiatrist, a daunting experience at the best, but necessary now that the individual's career was on the line. Fortunately his background was also taken into account; his previous military experience be it regimental, command or trade. Involvement in adventurous activities such as parachuting, pot-holing, mountaineering and the like are not undertaken voluntarily by the weak at heart. The interview was also devised to find out about potential problems in the subject's domestic life. An unhappy or unstable marriage could have disastrous results on an operator whilst on a tour of duty. Does he have to worry about an unfaithful wife or delinquent children?

In order to try and test the validity of selection one of the psychiatrists contacted all senior and chief ammunition technical officers who had served in Northern Ireland and asked them to rate independently their ten best and ten worst operators during their own tour of duty. An analysis of the groups showed:

Normal Training Course Performance	267	deaths 5
Poor Training Course Performance	33	deaths 5

The course performance included the pre-Northern Ireland EOD/IEDD training as well as the psychiatric testing.

In the period 1972 to 1976 a further breakdown of those who were psychiatrically tested showed the division between the ranks and training into the four groups in use at that time.

	A	B+	B–	C
Trained Officers	9	1	2	–
Trained S/NCOs	55	32	32	8
NCOs in Training	32	12	10	5
Soldier Applicants	50	11	15	19
Officer Applicants	9	9	6	2
Totals All Groups	175	65	65	34
	(52%)	(19%)	(19%)	(10%)

Note that it was accepted that A and B+ were the ideal operators and C was or should have been rejected; therefore some 29 per cent should not have been on active duty.

As previously mentioned, the first problem that had to be overcome was that of the psychologist and psychiatrist who had to become more objective. The second was that the earlier years had really been somewhat amateurish. A reappraisal of the actual tests was then made and these were adapted and improved to produce more information. The whole task then became more professional.

The need was to acquire more information to enable the interviewer, who only had some 20 to 30 minutes in which to use the written profiles to classify the subject, to obtain more background. In 1984 a two-part questionnaire was produced that provided biographical information. First there were questions about the subject's youth such as previous illnesses, disruptions to home life as a child, parents' divorce or death, poor appetite, bed wetting, what did the parents do, what were their interests, where did they live, what type of house and was there any evidence of delinquency? There were then questions about his present life such as, do you read, what sort of books, what are your criticisms of yourself and what sort of food do you like? In addition, in the mid-1980s, one of the main tests was changed and replaced by the California Personality Inventory (CPI) suitably adapted for use in the United Kingdom, and the whole lot was altered to enable students' answers to be fed into a computer and the analysis to be done automatically and in a very short space of time.

It was not until 1986 that the practice of testing personnel prior to acceptance for training was introduced and it is interesting that approximately 50 per cent of all potential trainees are now rejected mainly on the grounds of general competence. It is a fact of life that the job is now technically highly complicated and a reasonably high IQ level is necessary to cope with the scientific side of the trade.

The grading system also changed from alphabetical to numerical, Grades 1 to 5, similar to the original: Grade 1 – should be an officer, Grade 5 – get rid of the lunatic as soon as possible before he kills us all. Grades 2 to 4 were for more normal sort of folk, Grade 2 being a person well suited but having only one or two minor adverse characteristics, Grade 3 someone suitable but fallible as most of us really are and Grade 4 someone who should not, if possible, be employed. The result of an analysis of the groups indicated very few in Grade 1, more in Grade 2, a majority in Grade 3 (the norm), fewer in Grade 4 and very few in Grade 5. Grade 3 was eventually further divided into Grade 3+ and Grade 3–.

Now that the testing had become established it was possible to decide on potential trainees at an early age. As a person's character tends to continue to develop until about 25, for the average male, a candidate could fail as a recruit at age 18 and yet be acceptable on maturity at age 25. Although after maturity the basic character does not change materially it can be effected by life's rich pattern of experiences. A problem that can affect the results of psychometric testing for older men is the fact that they have held positions of authority and responsibility in which they have had to constantly make decisions. They do not tend to answer easily the 'Yes' or 'No' question; a somewhat pragmatic approach to life develops in which question or situation is considered before action.

In the course of research for this book many officers and men were consulted with a view to discovering their view on the benefits of psychometric testing and all that mumbo jumbo that is so popular with the 'shrinks'. Many found it hard to believe that the results from answering a few questions and a brief interview could in reality define their character strengths and weaknesses. Likewise, many eminent army psychiatrists and psychologists were asked their real opinion. It was not unexpected to find that they believe they can be very nearly perfect in their analysis.

I was a member of the trade in 1951 long before psychometric testing. My basic test consisted of fixing a plastic drawer handle to a piece of wood, typical of the times all the items were about knackered, screw heads worn out, screwdriver with a chewed up blade. I nearly failed when the wretched plastic handle broke in two pieces.

To try and see the modern tests for myself I managed to complete the four under scrutiny of Dr Stasu Labuc, a consultant psychologist with the Army Personnel Research Establishment. I duly completed the Labwick Personal Inventory about my school life and childhood, my thumb sucking and bed wetting, my sporting achievement, my eating, drinking and reading habits and finally my present medical condition. Fortunately as a male I did not have to reply to the questions specially designed for ladies.

I then visited Stasu at her home on a beautiful summer afternoon and completed the further three tests which included the California Personality Inventory with its 500 questions to be answered, true or false such as, 'do you enjoy sticking worms on fish hooks'; or the much more sinister, 'do you frequently count objects, such as panes of glass in windows, or carriages on a train or people in a carriage'.' (If you do it is a sure sign of obsession!)

Now although I have no axe to grind and the results of the test were for my eyes only, I still felt a degree of apprehension in exposing my soul to another, even one so attractive as Stasu. The tests took approximately one and a half hours to complete. Once the papers were handed over, the replies were fed into the dreaded computer and in about fifteen minutes the results were unavoidable. Should I leave now and continue to believe I was completely normal? One dreaded thought came to mind, if the results were put on paper my wife would insist on reading them. God knows she thinks I am mad now, why should I further reinforce her view? What if my secretary opened the mail and read it? Oh well, it really was too late now.

The dear doctor spent about fifteen minutes with her initial summary of my character, then she asked what I thought? She had got me about 95 per cent right: strongly independent, self reliant... I will miss out the sometimes selfish and self centred and concentrate on sincere, generous, honest and dependable, cautious, deliberate and strong willed. Perhaps my wife will insist I include the reference to garrulous (really I would have expected such a nice lady to have used 'talkative' – it must have been nerves) and hyperactive.

The question I asked before leaving, purely academic as I have no interest in rejoining the Army, having some years ago suffered the indignity of being rejected for the Home Defence Force, as too old, and really of little use to the infantry. If a grade had to be given for Bomb Disposal work what would it be? The answer was 'Grade 2', so at least the trip was not a complete waste of time.

My concern was for the benefits of psychometric testing and take some comfort in what has been stated as the ideal qualities of those involved in Bomb Disposal work. Perhaps it is the ability to withstand stress whilst retaining a high degree of effectiveness that is the most important factor for many senior managers, but the operator out in the field must also have a good judgement and foresight, quick learning, a logical and decisive mind yet still flexible. He must be self confident and prudent. He must obviously have technical knowledge and the ability to communicate and a personality that commands respect from those above as well as below. Perhaps the important additional attributes are that a man needs to be self-contained but not introverted and, in being decisive, he also must be aware that his life, and possibly others, may be dependent on his decisions and actions.

Anyone who has been privileged to visit the annual reunion of the holders of the Victoria and George Crosses will be struck by the fact that these very brave people look and seem so normal. They are elite in the eyes of others but not of themselves. So it is with the Ammunition Technicians and Technical Officers of the RAOC. We are as we become, due to our past formative years. It is a true statement to say 'Give me the boy and I will give you the man.' Two people in the same family, even if they attend the same school, will seldom be the same in character. From the age of four to five our character develops and is moulded by our circumstances and the people that we come in contact with.

Friends, our parents and relatives, our homes and the areas in which we live all have their influence upon us, also our interests and hobbies, sporting and recreational activities, our school, college, university and

DEMOLITION!

THE INSPECTING ORDNANCE OFFICER WHO DIRECTS THE DEMOLITION REQUIRES :- • AN AMMUNITION EXAMINER • AS TECHNICAL ASSISTANT • ONE MAN TO GUARD THE EXPLODER DYNAMO • • AND ASSIST IN WIRING • AND NORMALLY A MINIMUM OF 4 MEN TO POST AS LOOKOUTS • •

STAGE • 1 •

GENERAL PREPARATION •

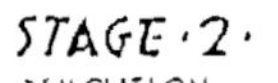

THE EXPLODER DYNAMO IS LOCKED • AND ITS CUSTODIAN HOLDS THE FIRING LEADS • ONE IN EACH HAND • •

THE • A • E • UNDERTAKES PRIMERING

• BOTH FIRING LEADS PEGGED AND ANCHORED • • I • O • O DIRECTS OPERATIONS • KEEPING SHARP LOOKOUT • •

STAGE • 2 •

DEMOLITION PREPARED • •

PERSONNEL NOW RETIRE TO SAFETY • NOTE THAT EXPLODER DYNAMO IS STILL LOCKED AND NO CONNECTIONS MADE • •

STAGE • 3 •

I • O • O UNLOCKS EXPLODER DYNAMO AND MAKES CONNECTION

STAGE • 4 •

I • O • O SOUNDS GENERAL 'TAKE COVER' WARNING FOR LOOKOUTS AND ALL ASSISTANTS • NO SPECTATORS •

STAGE • 5 •

I • O • O FIRES THE CHARGE

STAGE • 6 •

• I • O • O SOUNDS THE 'ALL CLEAR'

STAGE • 7 •

DIGGING PARTY DETAILED TO CHECK THAT PROJECTILE HAS BEEN DESTROYED • •

NOTICE!

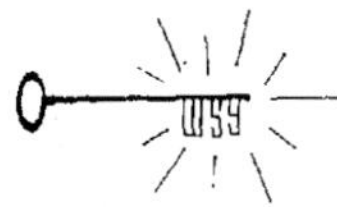

• THIS KEY IS KEPT BY THE I • O • O AND LOCKS THE EXPLODER DYNAMO PLEASE REALISE THAT AN OMISSION MEANS LOSS OF LIFE AND/OR COMMISSION •

(F.1714). F. & C. LTD. FIG. 2. • 1943 •

Above: Information and humour, 1945.

BREW

Opposite page top and centre: Mulberry Bush Bimingham, 1974.

Opposite page, bottom: Horse and Groom, Guildford, 1974.

Right and below: Tern Hill Barracks.

RECOMMENDATIONS FOR HONOURS OR AWARDS

1982

INSTRUCTIONS

DO NOT WRITE IN THIS MARGIN

1. To be completed in accordance with current instructions and forwarded to Ministry of Defence (MS3), Stanmore, Middlesex.
2. NOT to be used in connection with campaign stars or medals.
3. No abbreviations, except those officially authorized, will be used.
4. Whenever possible, typescript should be used.
5. This recommendation will NOT be considered unless the personal particulars of the individual are correctly completed.

If a casualty complete below:—	(For Ministry of Defence use only)
Killed in action on	Citation No.
Died of wounds on	File(s) D/DMS(B) 58/13/24.
Missing on	L.G. No. and date 13.12.77.
Prisoner of War on	Previous awards

Christian or Fore Name(s)	Surname	Delete as appropriate Regular/~~TAVR~~
KEITH FREDERICK ALEXANDER	ADAMS	

Personal/Army number	Sub. Rank	Present rank (if different from Sub. Rank)
23687207	WO 2	

Unit	Parent Regiment or Corps
321 EOD UNIT RAOC	RAOC.

Honour or Award for which recommended	Award for which finally approved by Ministry of Defence (For Ministry of Defence use only)
GEORGE MEDAL	GM.

Name (in blocks) and official designation of initiating officer

LIEUTENANT COLONEL D PATRICK CHIEF AMMUNITION TECHNICAL OFFICER

Date 13 JUNE 1977 Signature

Remarks of Brigade (or equivalent) Commander	Remarks of Divisional (or equivalent) Commander
Very strongly recommended	Very Strongly Recommended
Signature BRIGADIER D M WOODFORD CBE COMMANDER 3 INFANTRY BRIGADE	Signature MAJ GEN R B TRANT
Date 5 AUG 77 Place PORTADOWN	Date 22 AUG 77 Place LISBURN

Remarks of Corps (or equivalent) Commander	Remarks of Army (or equivalent) Commander
	Very Strongly Recommended
Signature	Signature LT GEN SIR DAVID HOUSE
Date Place	Date 24 AUG 77 Place LISBURN

Remarks of Commander-in-Chief or other Recommending Authority.

Signature Official Designation

Date Place

RESTRICTED

LG 13.12.77

Above: Recommendation for an award.

Top: Harrods, 1983.

Above: Manchester, 1996.

Right: Grand Hotel, Brighton, 1984.

Top: Westminster fire bomb.

Above: Hong Kong, 1967. Minutes before S/Sgt Les Reynolds was injured removing the devices at the bottom of the banner.

Left: Hong Kong, 1967. Major Emery being led away after a device exploded causing injury to his left hand.

Above: Territorials in training, Nottingham, 1995.

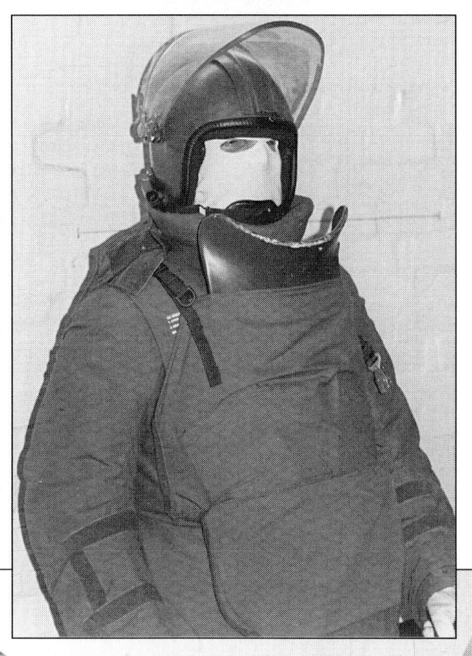

Left: The full kit.

Below: Pigstick in use.

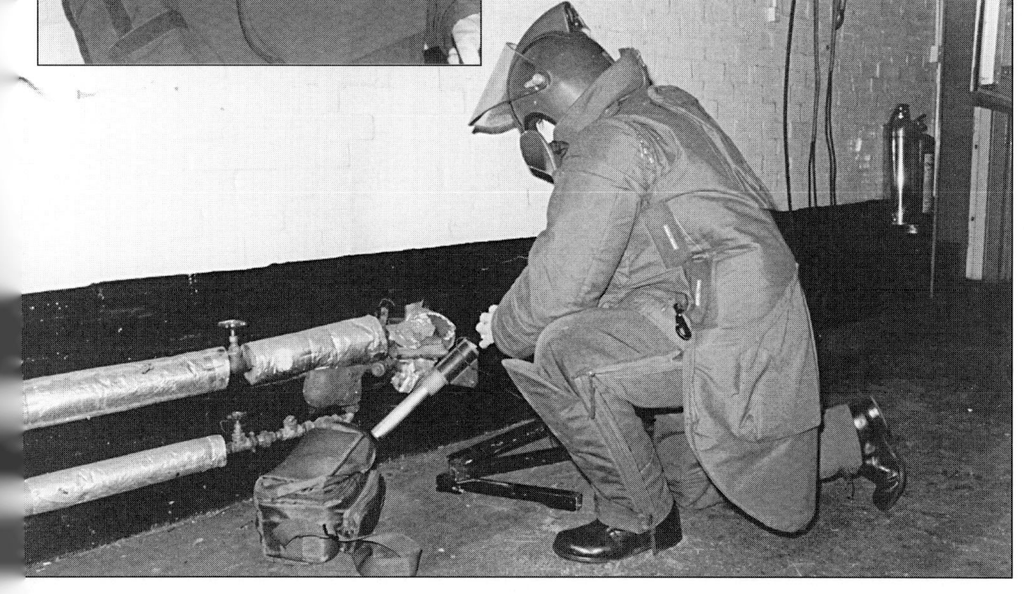

Above: Leyland Daf, 1996. **Below:** The vehicle interior.

Right: Pigstick, 1996.

Below: Buckeye, 1996.

Bottom: Buckeye at rest.

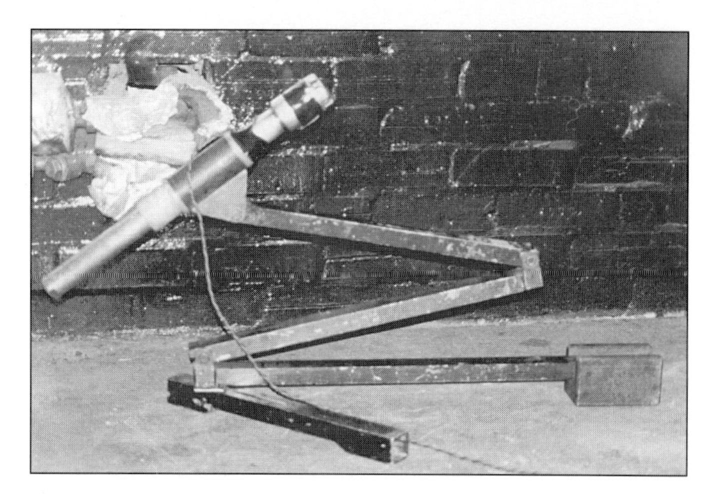

Left: Wheelbarrow armed and ready to go, 1996.

Below: An early model, a converted wheelchair, 1970.

Bottom: Wheelbarrow Mk I, April 1972.

Left: Wheelbarrow Mk II, 1972.

Lower left: Wheelbarrow Mk III, 1972.

Above: Wheelbarrow Mk V, 1973.

Below: Wheelbarrow Mk VI, 1975.

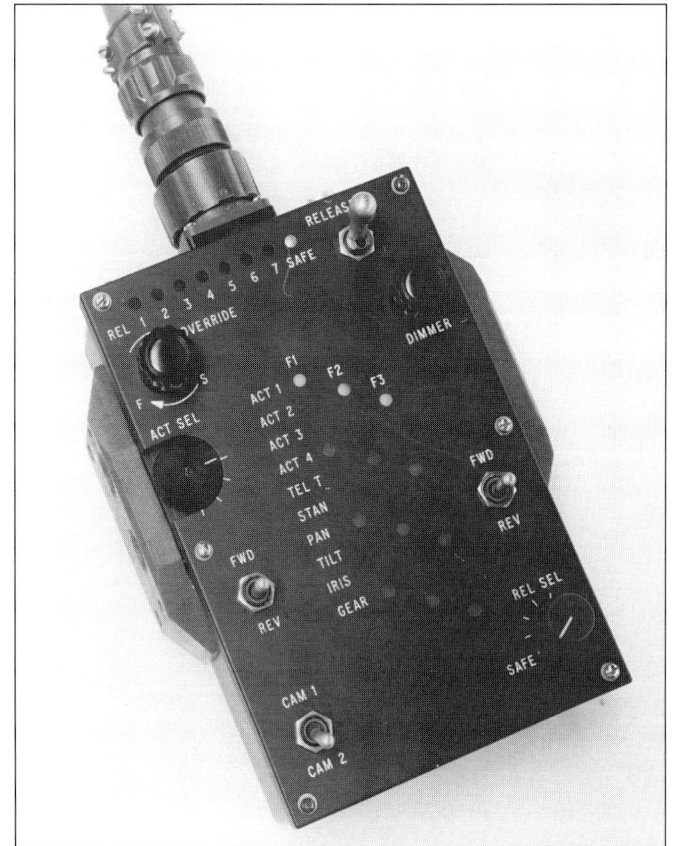

Above: Wheelbarrow Mk VII.

Left: The controls for the Wheelbarrow Mk VIII.

Right: A Mk VIII showing its manoeuvrability.

Below: A Mk VIII fully equiped.

B'mena
Coleraine
A 26
Cookstown
L'derry
M22
Belfast
M2
AIA 9060

Top left: Suspect car bomb Northern Ireland.

Bottom left: The railway train bomb, Northern Ireland, 1979.

Above: Car bomb, Lisburn, Northern Ireland, 1979.

Right: 120lb Semtex, Langenhagen Barracks, Germany, the largest single IRA bomb in Germany, 1990.

Above: Dungannon 1984 – a 200lb car bomb. Only the booster detonated.
Below: Armagh, 1984 – a partly detonated radio-controlled bomb.

employment, all help to mould our character. It is easy to respond to questions by camouflaging our 'outer shell' in order to create a good impression but our accents, clothing and smart appearance do not change the way we really are. People can respond in such a way as to convey the impression that they are assertive, are outgoing, have a social 'presence', are flexible, decisive and achievers. Perhaps this is what they would like to be, but in reality they may be submissive, introverted and easily manipulated by others. It is the training of the 'shrinks' that enables them to ferret out the truth. Enquiries into a subject's favourite sports and recreational interests will tell them a lot, not just about their physical fitness – others are responsible for this – but about their character. Football and cricket indicate good team membership. Rugby, for instance, indicates a team member who is prepared to get involved in a physical way. Sports such as long distance running, mountaineering and parachuting indicate someone who is courageous but happy working on their own. Trouble with authority at school or in teenage years might indicate a rebel who will not accept the necessary level of discipline for himself or from others.

At the end of the three-hour session someone else will have an excellent idea of what makes them the person they really are, and not the one that they would really like to be.

If they answer the questions with honesty, the result will probably be correct. If they are unsuccessful perhaps their failure has ensured that they do not find themselves in a situation beyond their capabilities, and perhaps they will not be placed into the position of being the cause of unnecessary loss of life, not only their own but others'.

All should now be aware that technical qualifications are not enough; it is the job of the 'shrinks' to decide which of us are daft enough to walk up to a suspect device in the certain knowledge that it could kill, and to carry on day after day, month after month when common sense urges us to go home and watch TV.

CHAPTER 11

EQUIPMENT

The equipment used by Ammunition Examiners of old all fitted neatly into a small ammunition box; the metal container for American belted rounds or the wooden inner liner from our own rifle ammunition was ideal. It only had to hold a couple of screwdrivers, a pair of pliers, some string and the eternal sticky tape. Later, with a few fish hooks (large size) and a bit more and stronger string, the first bomb disposal kit had arrived. The first real advances were made as a result of incidents in Cyprus and Hong Kong, especially the latter. Experiments were carried out with all sorts of sophisticated hardware including a type of bulldozer to collect devices in its front bucket like a strange road sweeper. They did not last long. Hong Kong saw the advent of 'equipped' Land Rovers, a form of flak jacket and a helmet.

The activity in Hong Kong prompted consideration of more adequate equipment to assist the technician in dealing with devices in a more sophisticated fashion, whilst at the same time affording a measure of protection. It is a regrettable fact that with a large device that has to be tackled 'hands on', a suit of armour does little more than contain one's earthly remains more or less in one place. Early experience indicated that perhaps initiation devices might be of the tilt type, that once armed meant it was impossible to remove the device without first neutralising the tilt mechanism. Early equipment included 'mechanical trepanning' to enable a hole to be cut in the package to gain access without moving it. Primitive gamma-ray inspection equipment was produced but was not really practical for use in the field.

Protective clothing was a must and was available in Hong Kong in the form of a type of helmet with a special Makralon face screen. The early use of a protective flak jacket was quickly followed by a full body suit complete with armoured panels. As will be appreciated from the photographs, this gives protection but is not enjoyable when the temperature is high. Clearance work in 1991 following the Gulf War saw operators employed by Royal Ordnance fully suited up and working in temperatures which reached 150°F. A twenty-minute stint was the most permitted. Some operators find it difficult to run in them, although, if needs must, it is amazing what can be achieved, remembering that the bomb suit weighs around 80lb when all the armoured panels are in place. One of the problems encountered with bomb suits is that they all smell. Being heavy and in constant use, they get a bit sweaty; the smell is universal and is no reflection on personal hygiene; it simply arises from sweat, dirt, oil, explosives and more sweat. However, they do provide some protection and even if part of it is in the mind it all helps.

It was not until the early 1970s that a piece of equipment was first produced to enable operators to view devices from a distance and to handle these in safety. As mentioned earlier five technicians died on duty over a short period of time when the terrorist activities really started in Northern Ireland. It was quickly realised that changes in procedure and equipment were vital otherwise operators would become a very scarce commodity. The ingenuity of the Ammunition Technician is well known and early on an electric wheelchair was 'borrowed' from a local hospital and adapted to carry a number of pieces of equipment. Complete with flashing lights and remote control, 'Little Willie' and the disrupter device 'Jack Horner' passed into history very quickly. 'Little Willie' was so named because 'Willie' had been painted on the back-rest of the original wheelchair.

In 1972 it was apparent that an effective disruption apparatus was required, to enable a charge to be fired at a suspect device. The intention was that the trigger be separated from the explosive content, thus rendering the device relatively safe to deal with. Initially experiments were carried out with a piece of naval equipment, the Sweatman Perforator. This had been developed for use against limpet mines, to separate them and their magnets from the hulls of ships. They had not really proved satisfactory for the Royal Navy. However, the principle was adopted by the Research and Development establishment. A light, three-part disrupter, which weighed less than 10lb, was produced late in the year; it was duly christened Pigstick. It was soon modified into a two-piece stainless steel model that weighed approximately 6lb. This has remained in service for most of the past twenty years.

It is a fact that when Mike, the civilian employee who was involved with the development of this equipment, delivered one of the prototypes to Northern Ireland, the ATO casually asked if his life insurance was up to date. When Mike asked why the ATO replied 'because then you can come and show us how it works'. For his work then, and later in the development of the equipment, he was awarded the MBE.

The concept of a robot now came to the fore; its need was obvious, its usefulness had been established and it was not too long before Wheelbarrow Mark I was in use. The necessary work to develop the robot was carried out by the Fighting Vehicles Research and Development Establishment in 1972. One of the early 'bolt on extras' requested was a means of fixing a hook and line onto motor cars that were suspected to contain explosive devices. The need on the day was to be able to fit a tow line, in safety, and to then move the car from its target area to one that was less dangerous and more convenient when a Wheelbarrow with a disrupter device could make its approach. The officer to whom this task was given must have had considerable DIY experience; he even had a remote controlled lawn mower, and no, he was no relation of Heath Robinson. Eventually the three-wheeled chassis of a Packhorse battery-operated Wheelbarrow was selected to form the basis of the equipment. It was adapted and fitted with a low level boom (to fit under a car chassis) and a spring loaded hook. It was tested and it worked. Wheelbarrow Mark I had arrived. You have to wonder what the local garden centre thought of this strange customer who ferreted away at old lawn mowers and the like before he went off with the Wheelbarrow or if they realise today their contribution towards the safety of technicians all over the world.

The device took 22 days to invent, design, develop and to produce, a remarkably short time. Wheelbarrow Mark I was an immediate success and an order for another six was issued within days.

Development and improvement soon followed. The Mark II versions contained two electric motors, one for drive and one for steering, a boom to allow explosive charges to be dropped into suspect cars, and various control relays and firing circuits. Mark III was developed within four days; this was on a better chassis and had four wheels to provide greater stability. Testing in use and liaison with design and manufacture was in very close harmony. Four-wheel-drive was now standard and as with the motor trade the bolt on optional extras grew in number. Towards the end of 1972, and remember the first Mark I was only produced early the same year, further improvements were requested by the 'never satisfied' technicians. The designer visited Belfast and was given the next two tasks, a closed circuit television camera to enable the operator to view a suspicious object from safety, before deciding how to tackle it, and the placing of a clamp to enable the Pigstick disrupter to be used and fired from the Wheelbarrow. Before the year end Mark III was in use in the Province. A major problem remained which the designer saw whilst in Northern Ireland was that when equipped with wheels the robot had difficulty mounting objects (and no, it was never intended to reproduce itself!)

A track was now needed to replace the wheels and ever innovative the designer obtained a pair of very heavy duty fan belts. Drive wheels and idle wheels were soon fitted, and a more efficient 24-volt electric system also improved Mark IV. Additional attention to the tracks and other improvements quickly resulted in the Mark V.

The original designer and the manufacturer, a retired lieutenant colonel tank gunnery officer, (at the research establishment) together with his skilled work force produced over 22 Mark V Wheelbarrow robots from 1971 to 1973 as well as the Mark VI and many more Marks II to IV, a remarkable achievement.

At the research establishment there was a civilian employed in the development of Wheelbarrows. Lofty was the only civilian who was privileged to wear the 'Felix' tie. This honour is restricted to technicians who have successfully dealt with a live bomb. Any personnel who have only dealt with hoaxes and false alarms, no matter how traumatic, can never wear the tie. Lofty got the honour by putting into practice his belief that you cannot be sure any device will work until you have tried it out yourself. He was such a frequent visitor to Belfast that he even had a bed reserved for him.

In June 1973 control of further development was taken over by a team of engineers on a far more formalised basis. Regrettably for security reasons it is not possible to name the retired lieutenant colonel or his staff but their contribution to the world-wide safety of all operators is unique, from an idea in 1971 to a sophisticated working aid in just two years. Let there be no doubt whatsoever that the death rate amongst EOD operators, not only in the RAOC but world-wide, would have been very considerable had it not been for these two basic tools, Pigstick and Wheelbarrow.

Not only have lives been saved but the equipment is now manufactured for sale world-wide. A Wheelbarrow in 1995 cost around £100,000.

Evolution was necessary at all times: the original closed circuit TV cameras only performed well in good sunlight, neither did they like explosions near at hand; these were replaced by an improved British camera. Radio control overcame the problems of umbilical cords that continually caught on objects. The design of the machine was such that if inadvertently blown up it could usually be back on the road within 24 hours. In the field the support from the REME was vital, their expert electrical and mechanical skills kept Wheelbarrow in everyday use. Together with the EOD operators, they fed back to the manufacturers a constant stream of ideas to develop and improve the machine. Great credit is due to the REME for their support to the team.

Wheelbarrow today is a very sophisticated device for dealing with the examination of suspect devices. A number of companies manufacture various designs some with tracks, some with wheels. All contain a large number of electric motors which enable the machine to move, and various arms and booms to hold a number of pieces of equipment to enable a variety of tasks to be handled from a safe distance. All contain lights and closed circuit television cameras. The controls are similar to those that most parents will have seen for model cars but far more complex. The efficient handling of these machines is a highly skilled task.

The early tracked models of Wheelbarrow, derived from the wheeled version which had difficulty climbing stairs, were hard to use in very confined spaces. It is reported that in the early days in attempting to deal with a device in a shop the machine became trapped by a swing door. An early modification was the addition of a device to enable nails to be driven into the floor to hold doors in the open position.

Pigstick, designed to disrupt the initiation device of a bomb, open a car boot or similar task, is standard now on most models. A modification to this was produced which was an extended version. It is reported that when first used to gain access to a bomb on the top deck of a bus, unable to tackle it from inside the vehicle, the Wheelbarrow was mounted on top of an armoured car, with the operator safely protected inside. All went well until the modified weapon was fired when both it and the Wheelbarrow disappeared backwards from the roof of the armoured car and at very high speed. A further modification was introduced shortly afterwards, with a Wheelbarrow mounted securely to the front of an armoured tractor.

New implements to enable devices to be tracked from a safe and remote distance were produced very early on. Technical failure is, however, a common problem when reasonably sophisticated equipment is used in an early design stage. During the early days of development there is a report of a very frustrated technician trying to deal with a large device in Northern Ireland. The road between the technician and the device was littered with three dead fork-lift trucks and five dead Wheelbarrows. The problem was eventually solved after a number of days when it became apparent that by some miracle the device had become attached to an old-fashioned hook and line. Was this divine intervention or perhaps a fed-up technician? The hook and line enabled the device to be moved to a safe place and to be destroyed.

A successor to Wheelbarrow was produced in 1977, intended to be an upmarket de luxe version. Being a bit too sophisticated for the routine in Northern Ireland, it did not replace Wheelbarrow. In place of the two single sections of track it had three sections to each side, it could 'walk' upstairs, it could pivot the top section and it had two separately controlled arms; one could control disrupters and shot-guns or other types of aids, the other had a grip so effective it could open a car door by remote control. At the cost ratio of one Marauder to four Wheelbarrows there was little real support for its introduction.

It is reported that an early version of Wheelbarrow was used by the police in the United States of America; it was apparently equipped with two shot-guns, spot lights, closed circuit TV and a loud hailer. It was intended to be used to deal with armed criminals in a siege situation. Up trundles the machine and when the operator has the victim on the screen – 'hands up you bugger or I'll shoot'. Perhaps it will be adapted for this use in the UK – who knows?

An eminent senior officer recalls that perhaps the most necessary equipment for all operators was the hook and line. It was far safer to use this even when an operator thought he recognised the bomb and knew from experience how to neutralise it. This plus a portable disrupter and a bomb suit were indispensable to him. This same officer recalls the day when one of his operators was attending to a final job before returning to the mainland. The suspect device was a dustbin. A selection of equipment was available but he selected Flat Sword. Asked why, the response was that it was the only thing he had not yet used. Now Flat Sword was a large piece of steel one foot wide by two feet long cut to a point at the front. Fixed to a stand and fired by a sheet of plastic explosive it had been developed to remotely cut open beer kegs. Being a fair minded officer he had to agree so Flat Sword was fired and neatly cut the dustbin in half; rubbish was scattered everywhere and the staff sergeant could go home with a gleam in his eye.

The spectacular result is an element of life that has to be controlled; there is the story of the AT who had to attend one of those milk churn incidents, not one or two, but a whole host of the wretched things, all full of home made explosives. Now he successfully neutralised and emptied all but one; the contents were all neatly bagged up just out of the way. When dealing with the final one, he had exhausted the supply of dismantling devices and obtained permission to blow the last one up. No one knows if he had forgotten about the effects of sympathetic explosion, or if he just needed to see what would occur if the lot went up. Well it did, including a nearby heap of bags, and I suppose he still has a gleam in his eye!

The sequel, a short time later, was the disgruntled local publican who, incidentally, must have seen the bombs laid in a location to take out a regular police patrol. His problem, which caused considerable agitation, was that the windows and the better part of his public house roof had sort of disappeared as a result of the blast. The senior officer present, serving with a famous regiment, soon put him in his place and presumably everyone went on their way with wonderment in their hearts.

Finally, all electric firing circuits are tested before a Wheelbarrow (or any other piece of equipment) is taken out for use. There is a long established rule and standard operating procedure for when this must be carried out. This story concerns a rather enthusiastic No. 1 and his inexperienced No. 2, a fearful combination. No. 1 prepared the detonators and electrical connectors, joined everything together and taped them all to his flak jacket, prior to arming the boom of Wheelbarrow. At this point his ever helpful No. 2 thought that he would double check the firing circuits. A single detonator on a flack jacket is not too bad but half a dozen produced rather bruised testicles! No doubt neither man will be so careless again.

CHAPTER 12

THE HOME GUARD AND THE TERRITORIAL ARMY

The Home Guard

It must not be overlooked that during the 1939–1945 period there were not only three services involved in what was then known as Bomb Disposal. In 1940 it was proposed that Auxiliary Bomb Disposal Squads be established. When the scheme was announced applications flooded in. The first course which included civilians was run in November 1940 at RAF Melksham. Later, due to a shortage of space for more RAF personnel, training was undertaken at the nearby Army Bomb Disposal School established in 1941, at Donnington Hall. It was not long after that that these auxiliaries, originally intended to protect their own factories, were formally absorbed into the Home Guard.

In the early days over 100 auxiliaries were trained at RAF Melksham and over 2,000 at the Donnington Hall school. By the end of 1940 two members of this valiant band had been awarded the George Medal. Mr Lee and Mr Cooke had become the first of many to hold this decoration for courage.

The Territorial Army

The Territorial Army has its origins in the Territorial Force created in 1908 to absorb the many militia, yeomanry and volunteer units which had grown up in the counties of Great Britain and in the nineteenth century provided the back-up for the Regular Army. Many of these had served with distinction in the Boer War and provided the framework for so many of the divisions which followed the British Expeditionary Force to France at the beginning of the First World War.

As an example of how volunteer units developed to meet the needs of the Army and the country, in 1859 the 5th Lancashire Rifle Volunteer Corps was established. In 1862 this became the Liverpool Rifles Volunteer Brigade, and in turn became the 2nd Volunteer Battalion of the King's (Liverpool) Regiment in 1888. The formation of the Territorial Force in 1908 saw the change to the 6th (Rifle) Battalion of the King's

(Liverpool) Regiment, The Liverpool Rifles. It served with distinction as one of some 28 battalions of the King's, during the First World War. A further name change occurred in 1936, to 38th (The King's) AA Battalion, RE. Early in 1940 it was transferred to the Royal Artillery. Prior to the start of the Second World War its strength was 52 officers and 1,575 other ranks, no small unit, even in those heady days.

Despite the changes of name, and affiliation to various branches from the infantry, engineers, artillery and even the Royal Corps of Transport, it remained to all its members The 6th Liverpool Rifles.

The period following the end of the Second World War saw the need to retain a large Army. The national serviceman had to join either the Civil Defence or the Territorial Army when his time with the colours had been completed. During this entire period there was no specialist unit which catered for the Ammunition Examiner of old, or the Ammunition Technician of today.

The first employment of AT and ATOs in TA units was in 1977. Two Replenishment Park (RP) companies were formed, 40 and 41 RP Companies RAOC (V), with an ammunition role as part of 1 Combat Supplies Battalion RAOC. Each of these companies had on its establishment a post for one ATO and four ATs, who could be TA (normally filled by recently ex-regular soldiers) or reservists. Sergeant Bill Brennan originally served with 41 Company and was continuing his TA service at the time of writing with 731 EOD Squadron Royal Logistic Corps (V). The two replenishment park companies were re-roled in 1983 as ammunition companies of 5 Ordnance Battalion, the complement of ATO/ATs remaining the same. It was not until 1986 that it was decided to establish a TA RAOC EOD Specialist Unit. At that time the RAOC had only 11 Battalion as a specialist EOD regular unit, with its companies and detachments in Northern Ireland and in various locations throughout the UK and it was considered that the TA unit should be part of this regular unit. The commanding officer for the regulars also became the Operational CO of the TA unit.

In order to get the TA units started, a letter was sent out to all recently discharged Ammunition Technicians and Ammunition Technical Officers, telling them about the new unit and asking whether they were interested in joining. So it was that in July 1986, at Corsham Depot, a corporal from the Royal Corps of Transport, Joe Wright, became the first full member of the then RAOC TA unit and began the task of organising the reception of approximately 25 men of all ranks. They had to have a medical inspection, get issued with kit and be sworn in. The officer largely responsible for the first TA unit was Lieutenant Colonel Courtney Green and without his determination, goodwill and support perhaps it would never have got off the ground. The first officer to have command of this strange body of the old and bold was Major Mike Thomason. So it all began.

The units were part of 11 Ordnance Battalion as three companies, numbered 531, 631 and 731. This system was based on the parent designated 321, 521, etc. The basic task of the TA was, and still is, to have available 60 teams of two men each to be available in time of war for all EOD tasks. The original intention was not to recruit and train TA operators but to use ex-regular ATOs and ATs. However, due to a grave shortage of ex-regulars wishing to join the TA, a change in policy had to be made. Recruitment straight from civilian life for training as EOD Operators began. However, in the same way as the training of regulars is of paramount importance, and very time consuming, so it is for TA and recruitment is either from former regular soldiers or fully trained members from other TA units, by transfer, that is, men and women who already have an army trade and who have undertaken the normal regimental training.

Potential recruits attend a weekend 'camp' where they are interviewed by a small panel, chaired by a squadron commander. The aim is not only to ensure that they can read and write but also that they are suitable candidates for training as EOD operators academically and physically; and, most importantly that their personality is such that they will fit into these small units. An essential requirement is that they show an ability to take and retain control at the site of an incident. They have to be potential leaders, assertive but not aggressive or bullying. As this is a weekend event they are also seen socially, as well as professionally. Selection is seen as a feather in anyone's cap!

As previously mentioned, there are three companies (or from 1993, following the formation of the Royal Logistics Corps, squadrons). The establishment of each squadron consists of six officers plus some 46 other ranks; a major in command, a captain as his second and four captains as troop commanders, a WO1, four WO2s, eight staff sergeants, five corporals and thirteen drivers plus a headquarters contingent of about six in various trades. Therefore the entire unit consists of a maximum of only 160 people of all ranks. A simple analysis also shows that promotion prospects are better than in the infantry. The 46 other ranks in a troop are split between 19 private soldiers and 27 NCOs, although, as in most TA units, when meeting for a weekend camp they usually work, eat and sleep together.

In the unit at time of writing there were a number of anomalies. There were two officer cadets were on the way to becoming EOD operators before being commissioned as second lieutenants and posted to a non-EOD unit, and a lieutenant who, because of his prior knowledge, experience and current job, was persuaded to take a commission. There was a staff sergeant, Ken Underwood, previously a regular Ammunition Technical Corporal, who joined the TA after leaving the Army. As a member of the TA he served as a TA sergeant for a year with the regular army EOD unit at Hereford during 1991/92. To be technically correct he was posted out of the TA for this year's service as an 'S' type regular soldier. However, he has the distinction of being the only TA EOD member to have actually dealt with a live device, although technically he was back in the regular Army. During his year's service he dealt with eighteen incendiary devices at one location. His experience is now used to train the younger men who are following on. As well as Ken Underwood, there were Joe Wright and Paul Walker, never regular ATs but fully trained TA EOD Class 1 operators.

Presently there are three stages of training in the unit for EOD operators.

Class 3 – training is provided entirely by the TA unit, but under the control of the regular regiment. Although the training will also cover the more advanced work, at this stage it is basically centred around the vehicle and the equipment. Personnel must know what it is, how it works and how to maintain it.

Class 2 – this trade classification is basically for the No. 2 in an EOD team, the person who does the work when on the job, ensuring that the right equipment is in the right place at the right time, and that it works. Such people are also trained in their own right in the disposal of conventional ordnance. Part of the training is by the TA, but they also attend a course at the Army School of Ammunition.

Class 1 – this is the pinnacle, these are fully trained EOD operators. They are expected to be able to act on their own at an incident, and to be capable of successfully dealing with whatever is put before them. To qualify they attend the EOD Operator Class 1 Course at the School of Ammunition.

A recent development has been the approval for those in the TA EOD Operators trade, when they qualify as Class 2 tradesmen, to wear a modified Ammunition Technician's badge, the same as their regular colleagues except that the A is changed to a V to indicate volunteer.

Readers may be interested in the time scale from joining the regiment to becoming a Class 1 tradesman. At present a reasonable student can expect to qualify after about six years' TA service. In the TA every member is expected to attend an annual camp. In this unit one annual camp every two years can be replaced by a specialist training course at the School of Ammunition. Additionally, there are probably around four to six weekend camps in the year, during which days are spent on technical training. One of these camps has to involve regimental duties; even EOD operators must be soldiers first!

The training cycle for the annual camps of approximately fifteen days is: 1st Year, Class 3; 2nd Year, Annual Camp; 3rd Year, Military Proficiency Course 1st Class; 4th Year, Class 2; 5th Year, Annual Camp; 6th Year, Class 1. The soldier must join the unit with Military Proficiency Certificate Class 2, and lots more! It is worth mentioning that at time of writing there was only one female Ammunition Technical Office in the regular Army, following a very recent change of policy. However, there are no such restrictions in the TA. Provided the individual is physically and mentally capable of doing the job, she can become a Class 1 operator and be a team No 1. In fact, in the unit at time of writing there were three ladies and, in the fullness of time, no doubt one of them will be the first to wear the coveted badge.

The role of the unit is to be able to field 20 two-man teams from each squadron, 60 in total, and under the 'Options for Change' programme, one of the three squadrons could become part of a Rapid Deployment Force.

As recruitment into these three small TA units is on a country-wide basis, men and women travel from far and wide to attend a training weekend, or annual camp. These venues are spread throughout the country at Hereford, Catterick, Chilwell, Grantham, Kineton, Bramley and Castlemartin, to name but a few. However, for annual training purposes, the three squadrons join together. Due to difficulties with travel, employment, holidays and family it seldom occurs that the entire unit collect together at the same time. It is more realistic to expect around 50/60 from the total of 160. This is one of the problems facing the TA in the 1990s. In addition to the training weekends and courses at the Army School of Ammunition, soldiers often manage to work their way onto all manner of other training sessions such as at the RAF School at Wittering, for the airfield clearance training.

I was privileged to attend one of the training weekends and met many of those present. I was greatly impressed by the keenness of the trainees, and the way in which the old and bold passed on their wide knowledge and experience. I was impressed with the military turn-out of those present, and by the way Major Kevin Callaghan, GM, QGM, organised the weekend and, with Major Norman Bonney TD, exercised command by total respect, in the highest tradition of any service.

CHAPTER 13

THE OTHER ARMS AND SERVICES

The Royal Navy

The activities and involvement of the Royal Navy have already been explained in this book, as has their involvement in bomb disposal when dealing with aircraft bombs during 1939/40. It was deemed that the Royal Navy had responsibility for all sea warfare equipment, not only in the sea and on the shoreline but also if these devices were dropped or found on the land. In the First World War sea mines had to be laid by ships but by 1939 mines were also laid from enemy aircraft which dropped them by parachute. As early as November 1939 some 200 mines had been removed and rendered safe.

As with the Royal Engineers (see below), whenever a new design was identified some poor technician was despatched post haste to catch it alive and find out how it worked. In November 1939 two naval officers, Lieutenants Lewis and Ouvry, received congratulations from the Admiralty for their technical and hazardous work.

In the early days clockwork devices were used that, once dropped from an aircraft, ran for five seconds and then stopped. On impact they ran for a further seventeen seconds before detonating the mine. The technician who met such a fuze on an unexploded mine knew that he had less than seventeen seconds in which to escape if the clock started ticking whilst he was dealing with the device. The medical stethoscope became part of the technician's kit, in order for him to listen for the clock, through the casing of the mine. It might seem easy to have escaped if the clock started ticking. It is not too difficult to run 100 yards in under seventeen seconds, but mines seldom landed on a running track. In a dock, in thick mud with little or no visibility it is a different matter, a dreadful and difficult situation.

Very early mines were not fitted with booby-traps, these came as a surprise in 1940 when six men died attempting to dismantle a mine. As the mine disposal experts became more successful, more mines with different anti-handling devices were discovered, designed to kill the technician should the mine fail in its main purpose.

It is recorded that one of the early naval experts was an American, Sub-Lieutenant D. L. Kauffman RNVR, who served for just over one year on bomb disposal work. In late 1941 he was injured and returned to Washington on leave. He was requested to establish the first US Bomb Disposal School, which was linked to their Mine Disposal School. Having left the Navy in the late 1930s due to poor eyesight, he was taken back in 1941. He eventually retired as an admiral! This marked the beginning of the long association of many foreign governments with the British service training systems, especially those dealing with Explosive Ordnance Disposal.

In the days prior to September 1940, three Distinguished Service Orders, two Distinguished Service Crosses and two Distinguished Service Medals were awarded to Royal Navy technicians in recognition of their heroic work. On 23 September 1940, HM King George VI announced that he had created a new award for gallantry, the George Cross, which has been featured in the awards from that time to all service ranks involved in Bomb Disposal work. The overall, magnificent, record of these for the work undertaken by the Royal Navy during the Second World War is:

George Cross	22
Distinguished Service Order	6
Distinguished Service Cross	12
George Medal	140
Distinguished Service Medal	18

Most of these men would have been members of the Mine Investigation or Mine Clearance Unit. The Royal Navy did not have a trade that specifically compared to the RAOC Ammunition Technician. Although they had to store ammunition in the same way as the other services, they did not have the same problems when disposing of misfires or other unserviceable shells and mines. These were simply 'dropped over the side', a practice which was discontinued many years ago.

As with all the other services, it is not possible to join the Navy with the sole intent of dealing with Explosive Ordnance Disposal. In the Royal Navy it was the trade of Clearance Diver that had responsibility for all types of underwater work connected to ordnance and mine clearance. This, of course, includes ordnance on ships and sea mines ashore. Responsibility also extends to the shore, up to the high water mark, all naval establishments and, more recently, the additional responsibility for offshore installations, such as the North Sea oil rigs.

Recruits join HMS *Raleigh* at Plymouth, a shore training establishment. There they receive their basic training in a way similar to recruits in all the services. After this basic training, recruits then undergo Part 2 training for their selected trade, at another shore establishment. Normally they will volunteer and complete a Ship's Diver's Course. Ship's divers are 'part-time, restricted in the depth they may work to and are responsible for minor engineering tasks, e.g. searching for items lost over the ship's side, but their primary role is searching the bottoms of ships for limpet mines. The keen ship's diver volunteers to join the Divers' Branch, and must then wait until he is selected for training. Ratings who successfully pass the course become a seaman diver. If the rating was not a seaman (he may have held the trade of cook, engineer or steward) when starting the Divers' sub-Branch Course, he must return to HMS *Raleigh*, for his Seamanship Course.

Initially, a sailor must volunteer to join the Divers' Branch and, in addition to good health, must have at least six months' very good conduct on his records, and at least eighteen months' service remaining to serve after completing his training. Additionally, he must be of above average intelligence. A candidate will have been considered by his previous commanding officer to have a strong sense of responsibility, be reliable, able to work unsupervised to a high standard and be suitable to work in small ships. Readers may note the similarity in basic character and personality to those involved in this trade in the other services. Finally, the candidate will further have to prove his suitability by passing general aptitude tests and rigorous tests of fitness – mud running tends to quickly weed out those who hoped for an easy life! Tests are carried out to ensure that the candidate can work underwater, in a totally dark environment. The preferred age group for this training is from 20 to 25 years old.

Normally, the sailor then returns to his ship until such time as a position becomes vacant on a Diver's Course, usually within twelve months.

The professional Diver's Course runs for fourteen weeks, on HMS *Nelson* (Gun Wharf). On satisfactory completion of the diving phase, the students move to the Defence EOD School for their introduction to Explosives Ordnance Disposal. During this intensive two-week course they learn how to search for, locate and identify underwater ordnance. Also during this period, they are taught the techniques of handling and using explosives. Students must pass both the EOD practical and written examinations at DEODS before they are awarded the rate of Seaman Diver and join the select body of men of the Divers' Branch. This elite trade was known as the Clearance Divers' Branch; however, the name was changed when the Royal Navy Operations Branch was formed, during the mid 1980s.

The Seaman (Diver) then progresses with the passage of time and practical experience to Able Seaman (Diver). The next stage in his career sees him returning to HMS *Nelson* for a further twelve weeks' diver training and four weeks' EOD training at the Defence EOD School. He now qualifies as a Leading Seaman (Diver). Progression to Petty Officer (Diver) involves a fifteen-week advanced diving course at HMS *Nelson*, with ten weeks at the Defence EOD School. When a Petty Officer (Diver) is drafted to a shore-based diving unit he is required to become an IEDD (Improvised Explosive Device Disposal) operator; therefore he attends a further one-week introductory course at DEODS followed by three weeks' advanced IEDD training at the Army School of Ammunition.

IEDD operators fall into two categories, No. 1 and No. 2 operators. In the Royal Navy No. 2s are Able Seaman (Diver) and Leading Seaman (Diver) who have undertaken the relevant training, whilst No. 1 Operators are Petty Officers (Diver) and the more senior ratings. Again, this is similar to the other services. To be able to deal with devices the RN Petty Officer (Diver) has to be licensed by the RAOC, and to be relicensed every six months, in exactly the same way as all the other services.

It is difficult to compare the 'ratings' in the Navy to an equivalent Army rank. A petty officer is similar in status to a sergeant, a warrant officer is equivalent to a WO1, whilst a chief petty officer falls somewhere between staff sergeant and WO2.

Readers will be well aware of the recent cut backs in the armed forces. Not so many years ago the Royal Navy was the most powerful in the world, and had bases literally all over the world. At these bases and on these ships there were divers, many of them deep water divers, who were the forerunners of the clearance diver and diver of today. For security reasons it is not permissible to detail the present locations of today's divers, or the particular responsibilities of their various units, but they continue to deal with conventional ordnance used by the Royal Navy, in exactly the same way as during the past 50 or more years, and with Improvised Explosive Devices.

As previously explained, the Royal Navy is responsible for all IED booby-traps and other explosive hazards which are below the high water mark. They operate on ships at sea, on off-shore installations, such as oil rigs, and they are located on any naval property.

In times of peace all three services provide support to the civil police, to deal with IED incidents throughout the UK. Their resources are called upon by the police through recognised channels. The priority of the incident is designated and an IEDD team is tasked to investigate and effect disposal.

Standard practice is that the team that can reach the incident most quickly will be tasked, unless special circumstances apply, such as an underwater item or when information regarding the problem indicates another specialist need. No team from any of the services will be tasked to an incident unless the operator is currently licensed by the RAOC (now the RLC). These conditions apply to the Army, Navy and Air Force.

As a Seaman progresses with his chosen career through a variety of ranks he may retire at the end of his particular period of engagement or, if he is a Warrant Officer, he can serve until the age of 50 or so. Indeed, some Chief Petty Officers also serve until aged 50. As with the other services, there are a considerable number of qualified and experienced men in the trade. In 1993 the total was just over 300 in the ranks, as follows:

Warrant Officer Diver	8
Chief Petty Officer	25
Petty Officer Diver	54
Leading Seaman Diver	79
Able Seaman Diver	140

After service there are a number of civilian opportunities. The training and experience, not only technical but in character and management skills, mean that a retired diver is unlikely to be unemployed for very long. As with all the services, there is a brotherhood of 'old boys' that extends far and wide, who know each other and employ those that they know.

The badge of the trade of Diver, Royal Navy, indicates both the trade and rank of the holder and is worn on the right sleeve, above the elbow. The real specialist trade starts with the Able Seaman Diver, helmet and one star; Leading Seaman Diver has a helmet with star above and below; Petty Officer Diver has helmet and crown; Chief Petty Officer Diver also has a helmet and crown but on either lapel of his jacket; the Warrant Officer wears the helmet and crown on the right lower sleeve of his jacket.

The Royal Navy used their clearance teams during the Falklands War. In the past the emphasis was perhaps more on an underwater threat. In the Falklands, in addition to dealing with sea mines and beach clearance, they had to deal with unexploded bombs on British warships. High numbers of air attacks successfully delivered their bombs to the targets, yet a surprisingly high number failed to explode. These were successfully tackled by teams from the Royal Navy. Fleet Chief Petty Officer Fellows had the task of dealing with a damaged bomb lodged close to a missile magazine on HMS *Antrim.* This required ten hours of hazardous and difficult effort whilst under constant attack by the Argentinian Air Force. The bomb was safely removed and dumped into deep water.

Also, readers may remember the disaster that overtook RFA *Sir Galahad,* which was bombed and destroyed in June 1982, with a high and tragic loss of life. The vessel had been a high priority to the Argentinian Air Force, and under constant attack. In May a 1,000lb bomb struck and failed to explode. In difficult surroundings it was disposed of by Lieutenant N. Bruen, Royal Navy.

This book is primarily about the RAOC and RLC Ammunition Technician, and the references to the other services are for comparison and even though my references to incidents and gallantry are primarily about those Corps, I have included specific other services at times. The awards of the Queen's Gallantry Medal to Warrant Officer Kidman for making safe

Seadart missiles after a collision in the Gulf in 1989, and to Warrant Officer Oulds for clearing a wartime German mine from a tug's anchor in Wales in 1990, indicate the continuing need for brave men such as these.

The Army and Air Force have already confirmed the quantity of ordnance remaining in the UK from the Second World War, which it is their responsibility to destroy. The Royal Navy state that around 200,000 mines remain in the seas around our coastline which have to be dealt with on a regular basis. The services of the Divers' Branch will be needed for many more years to come.

The Royal Engineers

During the First World War the number of aircraft bombs that were dropped on the British mainland amounted to just over 8,500. Some 500 of these failed to explode. The problem of UXBs was therefore very small and there was no real problem. At this time UXBs were dealt with by the Army Ordnance Corps, in addition to their routine tasks of disposal of all other land service munitions. Although little action was taken prior to the start of the Second World War, in 1936 the police were notified, in a Home Office instruction, that the Royal Army Ordnance Corps would be responsible for the general disposal of all unexploded bombs, unless a suitable representative of the Royal Navy or Royal Air Force was available.

As the clouds of war grew darker someone in the War Office realised that most qualified RAOC personnel would be overseas on duty. The experience gained in the First World War called for ammunition staff of all grades to be in place to deal with problems that arose 'near to the front'. Not unusually for the times there arose a conflict between Home Office and the War Department and no satisfactory resolution was achieved. This unsatisfactory situation continued and not too many people appreciated either the number of bombs that could and would be delivered, or the complexity of modern fuzes. However, progress was made and in traditional style a committee was formed to look into the problem.

After various fanciful suggestions such as a special force recruited from the British Legion, old soldiers past their 'sell by date', or using the new ARP, eventually an element of common sense was applied but still without a real sense of urgency. The Prime Minister was continuing to assure those who would listen that all was well. No one in government had any appreciation of the potential problem. Even the experience in the Spanish Civil War was discounted – 'Never happen here old chap.' The Air Ministry could cope: 'What? Three men a team, quite enough. Train them in a day, what?' The scene can be imagined.

As a temporary measure it was decided that the War Office would be made responsible, until a specially trained force could be recruited. The major breakthrough was that someone took the view that the task should be undertaken by the Royal Engineers. They had been trained in the use of explosives for demolition work, also they were trained engineers who were experienced in construction, mining and general excavation work. Small teams were quickly established with the brief to carry out the demolition of all unexploded bombs found on the UK mainland.

By November 1939 Bomb Disposal Parties, Royal Engineers were formed, comprising a junior NCO and two men with little in the way of equipment or training and off they were sent to those locations that the authorities felt would be sought out by the *Luftwaffe.* At this time the Royal Navy and Royal Air Force also established their own squads, to deal with bombs on their own service property.

Early in 1940, the Royal Engineers started to increase the number of Bomb Disposal sections; by the middle of the year there were over 200. By August 1940 the Germans were within easy bombing range of the UK mainland; most of Europe had by then fallen. The Battle of Britain started and bombing became a fact of everyday life. The War Office woke up and bomb disposal was handed over to GHQ Home Forces. A meeting held in London, chaired by the Royal Engineers, laid down the guidelines, training, intelligence and technical support. This meeting was followed days later by the formation of the Bomb Disposal Directorate.

Those who saw the TV series *Danger UXB* will appreciate the complications of these early days. The Royal Engineers had a mammoth task and had to cope with shortage of personnel, poor conditions of their billets, lack of support facilities and the added problem of dealing with a very large quantity of unexploded bombs, in all sorts of strange places, hanging in space and buried deep in the ground. They constantly had to deal with new fuzes, anti-handling devices and delayed action fuzes where the pre-set time for detonation could not even be guessed at.

Very soon a research committee was established to deal with the technical problems. Very quickly technical advice was available for cutting into the bomb casing and steaming out the explosive and methods to 'freeze' the fuze. Equipment was invented to remove fuzes. Regrettably during this time the Royal Engineers, like the RAOC in Northern Ireland in 1970, lost a number of very heroic men. As quickly as safe procedures were formulated the Germans countered with anti-handling devices.

In the early days of the Second World War incidents involving unexploded bombs were placed into four categories:

A Immediate removal essential for the war effort.

B As in A, above, but slightly less urgent.

C Removal necessary in the interest of the community.

D UXB in open country, removal necessary but can be left.

This was the basis of dealing with the problem and similar priority is still placed on terrorist devices today, although now the risks to the technician are also borne in mind.

The procedure in all 'Bomb Disposal' work was then and still is today, the man at the sharp end is connected by telephone, or radio, to his back-up team. Every move he makes is reported back down the line. If he turns the screw to the left and is blown up then the next time the technician turns it to the right and so on. Any new devices and strange modifications and how to deal with them were very quickly passed to all teams.

The first fully co-ordinated RE and RAOC Bomb Disposal team operated in Malta in mid-1940. At that time Captain R. L. Jephson-Jones RAOC and Lieutenant Eastman RAOC, both ammunition trained, joined together with a team from the Royal Engineers. Both these officers were awarded the George Cross in December 1940. These RAOC officers were replaced by Lieutenant E. E. Talbot RE GC, to whom this decoration had been awarded for work in Wales earlier that year. Apart from the awards for bravery to many Royal Engineers for their bomb disposal work during and after the war, it should be recorded that some 150 were killed on duty between 1943 and 1947.

Before leaving the Second World War period there were two other interesting developments. In 1944/45 diving teams were established to deal with underwater devices that fell to the Royal Engineers under the clearance rules. This training has been continued right up to present times and is necessary when aircraft bombs are discovered in canals, lakes and the like. In the services it has been customary to train soldiers prior to their release into civilian life with a pre-release course. A very useful course was to train RE disposal squad personnel in the art of lock picking and safe and strong-room breaking. This skill was required by the Allies to gain access to German headquarters secret information as the war progressed into Germany. There is no record of this useful skill being used by those men for unlawful purposes when they returned home after the war.

A total of one million bombs, mines and other explosive ordnance was dealt with by the Royal Engineers in the period mid-1944 to mid-1945 and this excludes booby-traps and unused non-damaged stores – a remarkable feat.

After the end of the war although the rain of bombs had ceased, the work of clearance had to continue. As the work of rebuilding started so finds of deeply buried bombs continued in later years; as these rebuilt premises were demolished to make way for even larger buildings which required deeper foundations more bombs came to light.

The Royal Engineers are responsible for battlefield clearance. The duty of laying minefields has always been with the Royal Engineers, and the removal of these devices together with the general explosive rubbish left lying around after a conflict has also been theirs. During the Second World War mainland UK was, in effect, a fortified island, extensive minefields having been laid around the coast. A little-known fact is that from during the war right up to date a large part of the clearance work necessary within the UK has been undertaken by a highly skilled dedicated group of civilians. This band was originally composed largely of Ukrainian former prisoners-of-war, who for various reasons did not wish to return home in the late 1940s. For well over forty years they have worked in all weathers, in some dreadful places and conditions, all the time finding and disposing of the explosive devices to make the country safe for the population once more. The country owes this civilian part of the Royal Engineers a great debt.

A Royal Engineers bomb disposal section was based in Kure in 1952 and dealt with a number of unexploded devices, including three influence sea mines, both in Korea and Japan. From 1953 until the end of the

Korean war, the bomb disposal requirement was met by three established posts in 28 Engineer Regiment in Korea.

The period of the late 1960s was when some major effort was taken to clear some of the old sites in the more exotic parts of the world. The efforts of the RAOC have been recorded; similar work was undertaken by the Royal Engineers. In 1965 a team went to Betio in the Gilbert and Ellice Islands where a considerable quantity of Japanese ordnance had been stored in some 50 underground bunkers, most of which had collapsed, mainly due to the bombardment prior to the capture of the island during the war, but partly with the passage of time. As with most of the Pacific islands, after the war considerable effort had gone into the usual battlefield clearance a short time after the conflict by the army on the ground; in most cases this was efficiently carried out by the American service, but the task was such that some areas had to be left; this was one such area. The explosive ordnance found in these bunkers had succumbed to the effects of war damage and tropical deterioration. The explosive fillings had been broken down to such a degree that not only was there extensive exuded liquid, dangerous enough, but the crystallised form was present as well, which is extremely sensitive to friction. A considerable amount of explosives were removed and safely dumped at sea, some 100 tons in total, but in the time available the two Royal Engineers were unable to complete the task. For these two tasks both Major Qualtrough and Sergeant Cooke were awarded the George Medal. Ten years later a much larger joint services team completed the work on the islands.

A similar task fell to the Royal Engineers on the beautiful island of Penang, off the west coast of Malaya. There remained there a collection of tunnels and bunkers that had been used by the Japanese as mine and bomb dumps. Part of these had been cleared in 1950 to stop the contents falling into the hands of the terrorists but a considerable quantity of explosive ordnance remained. Periodic efforts were made to reduce this. Two men of 11 Independent Field Squadron Royal Engineers were killed on this task in 1957. The material was in a dreadful condition and it took a considerable period of hard work in poor conditions to locate the explosives, remove them and safely dispose of the major quantity. Penang was an important holiday island for the Malay States and final clearance work was completed in 1967 by a 12-man team from the Engineers. A George Medal, and two British Empire Medals were awarded, such was the extent of danger involved in this clearance work.

The Falklands War was the most recent major conflict involving British forces in which extensive air attack was launched by the enemy. It was also the first that received full television coverage when the true heroic exploit was known by the world shortly after the incident. It is somewhat unusual for one service to be active on the grounds of another. HMS *Argonaut* was hit by two 1,000lb bombs: one lodged in the boiler room, the other in the forward missile magazine resting between two missiles. An RE EOD team was readily available and was put on board the ship. WO2 Phillips and Staff Sergeant Prescott successfully removed the fuze from the bomb in the boiler room. It has to be remembered that training did not cover working on board a ship in strange, unfamiliar very cramped surroundings. In the typical ways of the service the two Royal Engineers, having now had this experience, were sent to deal with two bombs on HMS *Antelope.* The Captain of HMS *Antelope* realised the danger and cleared his crew away from the area. Attempts to defuze the bomb by remote means proved difficult, on the fourth attempt the bomb exploded. Staff Sergeant Prescott was killed and WO2 Phillips seriously injured. The ship had to be abandoned and sank, with minimum casualties. WO2 Phillips was awarded the Distinguished Service Cross (DSC), an unusual enough award for a soldier. Even more unusual was the posthumous Conspicuous Gallantry Medal (CGM) awarded to Staff Sergeant J. Prescott. This is a very rare naval decoration, awarded on active service for heroic and gallant conduct of a degree which falls just short of the award of the Victoria Cross. So rare is it that only 245 have been awarded since its inception in 1855.

This sad loss gave the Royal Engineers a problem and a replacement team had to be sent out from the UK as a matter of urgency. The work necessary to clear the Falklands, and with particular priority to the main areas of population, was considerable. Stanley was in fact by this time an enormous ammunition depot; all available accommodation had been used for the storage of all sorts of explosive ordnance, from missiles to small arms ammunition. It all had to be collected together and sorted; sound usable ordnance had to be stored; damaged and unserviceable items collected together and safely destroyed. For the first time for many years work was involved with clearing booby-traps before tackling the main jobs. Once the Royal Engineer search teams had completed their work and the ammunition declared free from booby-traps it was then handed over to the ammunition technicians of the RAOC who became responsible for its ultimate end.

During the period from June to September 1982 the Royal Engineers cleared well over 10,000 unexploded ordnance items. Some ten years after the end of the Falklands War there was still an EOD team based at Stanley, men from 33 Engineer Regiment (EOD) having continually served short tours on their hazardous mine clearance work. There were similar EOD teams from the RAOC and Royal Air Force. The Royal Engineers have adapted the conventional Wheelbarrow Mark VIII for work in the minefields. The equipment has been renamed REDFIRE (Remote Equipment Demolition Falklands Islands Royal Engineers) to identify its new use. This equipment has been adapted to scoop-up and burn out charges or to place explosive charges alongside mines for their individual destruction.

The Argentine forces laid around 25,000 mines during the war of 1982. The majority of these are now in areas where the 'importance' of clearance is not too great and they remain today; however, since 1982 some 500,000 acres of land have been cleared and the count of all items from grenades to missiles destroyed exceeds 45,000. The work will continue into the future.

33 Engineer Regiment (EOD) Royal Engineers

33 Engineer Regiment (EOD) Royal Engineers is the main unit of the Royal Engineers that has the permanent task of dealing with UXBs and similar problems in the UK and abroad. The Regiment is responsible for air delivery weapons whilst 11 Ordnance Battalion deals with the conventional and Improvised Explosive Devices. 33 Regiment is the last remaining regular descendant of the units that dealt with bomb disposal during the Second World War. This Regiment proudly wears its special battle honour, a yellow and blue bomb on a red background, worn on the sleeve of every serving member of the regiment. A trade badge for the bomb disposal engineer was introduced in 1989 and all duly qualified combat engineers

wear this slightly smaller yellow and blue bomb on a khaki background. The men of the regiment normally serve for three years on disposal work and then return to their main trade as combat engineers within another unit of the Corps. There is now also a Territorial Army EOD Regiment, 101 Engineer Regiment (EOD) (V), based in London.

Royal Engineers EOD units are continually searching and clearing areas of the UK where there is a possibility of unexploded ordnance. They still attend to wartime bombs found during rebuilding work around the country, and have recently cleared a large area of pipe mines from an old airfield site in the south. The volume of work remaining within the UK is estimated to keep men active for at least another 40 years.

Improvised Explosive Device Disposal (IEDD) is the primary responsibility of the Royal Logistic Corps, but 33 Engineer Regiment have a battlefield capability and there are members of the regiment who have undertaken the IEDD training both at the Defence EOD School, and at the Royal Logistic Corps School of Ammunition. These operators are licensed by the RLC and have to undertake regular testing for renewal of their licences. They undertake IEDD work in the UK, and hold a team on ten-minute standby in Essex, their new base since relocating recently from Kent, to cover the south-east area of England.

The regiment embodies all the skills of the Royal Engineers and includes parachutists, divers and plant operators, plus the bomb disposal skills, which makes the regiment unique in the British Army. Unlike the RLC the Royal Engineers do not have to undergo psychometric testing and unlike the RLC they have two female members who have passed the necessary training courses and who are qualified to deal with all EOD (as of 1992).

As a highly compact and specialist unit the regiment currently consists of three regular squadrons; one handles the remote controlled plant and equipment, another airfields, search and IEDD whilst the third deals with battlefield clearance, having an airborne, a marine and a mobile troop. During 1989 this clearance troop spent four months in Gibraltar, two months in Cyprus and two months in Belize. If you can stand the stress it's not a bad way to see the world.

The battlefield clearance task in Gibraltar was not the norm. A new landfill was being undertaken when an explosion damaged the suction pipe on the dredger. This indicated explosive ordnance, and an examination of the area showed an assortment of suspect items. The troop had the job of searching all the infill material to remove any suspect hardware. After four months the items recovered ranged from Roman through medieval to modern, stone cannon balls to modern shell and bombs. The regiment has seen service in 1990 and 1991, in Kuwait, originally in support of 1 (UK) Armoured Division, and later in support of Royal Ordnance Plc on 'Operation Pinseeker'.

Another of the Royal Engineers' tasks is 'Search'. As highly skilled engineers, construction workers and surveyors they know all about buildings, their design and construction. It therefore falls to them both to provide teams and to train all arms in searching for explosive devices, booby-traps and the like. Search advisors attend a four-week training course, two weeks in a classroom and two weeks' practical training with a team. In addition they are trained to search buildings to ensure that a long delay time device has not been planted, another vital task in this age of high technology for the terrorist.

Awards for gallantry to Royal Engineers bomb disposal and EOD specialists during the period 1940 – 1982 have been:

Distinguished Service Cross	1
Conspicuous Gallantry Medal	1
George Cross	13
George Medal	115

The Royal Air Force

The task of storage, inspection and delivery of all RAF ammunition and aircraft bombs prior to 1939 rested with the Royal Army Ordnance Corps. The types of weapons used by the RAF were really only military machine-guns, adapted and fitted to aeroplanes. Bombs were little more than large hand held grenades dropped by a simple wire control; the entire contraption fitted outside the plane. Little had changed since 1914–18. The RAF were only too well aware that their bombs dropped on training ranges often failed to explode. The responsibility of dealing with these was with demolition squads consisting of warrant officers and senior NCO armourers. These men, then and now, undertook long and comprehensive training in all aspects of the weapons, ammunition, bombs and related fuzes that were used by their own service.

The Second World War saw the RAF react probably a little more quickly than the other services. By mid-1940 they had established a special one-week course in bomb disposal at their Armament School in Manby, and approximately 200 technicians had been trained by the end of September and dispersed around some 80 RAF stations. At that time reports indicated that some 250 unexploded bombs were located at RAF stations, waiting to be dealt with by experts. By May 1941 the number of technical experts had risen from 200 to nearer 500. They had successfully dealt with over 1,500 bombs.

The RAF were responsible for all enemy bombs on their own property, all bombs within and around any crashed plane of whatever nationality, German, British or American, together with allied weapons on public property. These remain the basic responsibilities of the RAF bomb disposal expert.

During the Second World War, the RAF Bomb Disposal technicians dealt with over 83,000 bombs within the UK and over 92,000 bombs in Europe. After the end of the war a further considerable tonnage was either destroyed or dumped at sea; in the region of 200,000 tons were involved, no mean feat!

In the period towards the end of the war some 400 bomb disposal technicians served in Europe; their task was to clear all explosive ordnance from airfields as they were captured by the Allies. In itself this sounds a rather inoffensive duty, but each airfield had been extensively bombed by the Allies as the war progressed. Not all the German ordnance was in neat heaps or in bunkers awaiting disposal; much was scattered far and wide and was in a dangerous condition that required considerable bravery and dedication to handle day after day.

Perhaps a less attractive job that the RAF had to resolve was in North Wales. During 1941 RAF Llanberis was used as an explosives storage site. Later it was used as a dumping and destruction ground for a considerable tonnage of assorted explosive rubbish. Unless this sort of junk is disposed of properly in the first place, before too long the job has grown to major and dangerous proportions. So it was at Llanberis. In 1969 orders were given to clear the site. To most readers this might appear a simple enough task but they have to imagine a desolate grey mountainous area in North Wales, wet and windy, to say the least, with explosive devices lying on the ledges that surround the deep slate quarry and the deep water below full of rotting bombs.

The first task was to train the bomb disposal teams in rock climbing. Fortunately the RAF mountain rescue teams were available and another skill was soon passed on. This major task, although the responsibility of the RAF, soon became a multi-service task. Royal Engineers were called in to construct the required access roads as what is suitable for use by quarrymasters over which to transport slate and stone is hardly suitable for highly sensitive explosives. The Royal Navy was brought in to provide clearance divers to work under water in the base of the quarry. Over 20 million gallons of water had to be pumped out, together with the sludge of decades. Some 80,000 tons of slate and quarry debris had to be moved. This major task took from 1969 to 1975 and during this period approximately 350 tons of explosive items of various types were collected, removed and safely disposed of, together with around 1,400 tons of non-explosive ordnance debris.

Many redundant training areas had to be cleared following the end of hostilities; the nation wanted access to the countryside and could not accept or understand the continued need to have 'Keep Out' notices now that the war was over. Some 70 locations were known to require clearance and most of these had been sorted out by the early 1950s; as time passed more areas were added to the list. At times it seemed rather like an endless cycle; work continued, in fact, virtually right up to date. Now it is a regular event to ensure that bombing ranges in current use are kept more or less clear as training continues.

Perhaps the scale of the task can best be recorded by some examples. In 1954 over 2,000 acres were cleared and 35,000 items recovered. In 1964 a similar area was cleared, including over 200 acres on the Isle of Man. In 1961 over 4,000 acres in Scotland was pronounced safe once more. At times this must seem an endless task; even today, given the current manpower available, the RAF reckon to have over thirty years' backlog of UK range clearance work.

The RAF EOD teams were active in the Falklands: Flight Lieutenant Swan and Warrant Officer Trafford landed at Ajax Bay and immediately started work. Disposal work was carried out on four unexploded bombs; two outside the Mobile Surgical Unit were demolished and a further two actually inside the Surgical Unit proved impossible to deal with in the short term. Patients could not be evacuated and to prove that he truly believed the bombs would not explode one officer moved in and slept within a few feet of the monsters. During the attack on the hospital a nearby ammunition dump was hit and the contents scattered all around, in particular all over the helicopter landing area which was essential for the delivery of the injured. The RAF team set to and manually cleared the landing area to bring it back into service within two hours, one of the tasks intentionally covered in their training.

The airfield at Goose Green was captured by 2nd Battalion The Parachute Regiment, and the RAF, RAOC and RE were asked to make it safe as quickly as possible as it was required. This was where a quantity of weapons were found that proved to contain napalm which was not in very good condition. A total of seventeen tons of explosives were cleared and destroyed before the airfield could be brought back into service.

As with all the services it is not possible to join the Royal Air Force to specialise in 'bomb disposal'. A person joins and undertakes the normal basic training, with several aptitude tests of a general and technical nature. The recruit's performance plus the results of the tests determines which branch of the service he or she enters. Trade Group I is the mechanical aircraft trade including weapons. The initial training covers a period of 25 weeks and the successful students pass with the trade of Engineering Mechanic (Weapons). They are posted to units and are then steered into gradual progression in the trade for approximately two years. They then return to Cosford for a further period, currently approximately 37 weeks, increased some short time ago to provide training to the B Tech qualification. At no time during this period of service is any specific Explosive Ordnance Disposal training given. However in the RAF this trade not only covers the weapons but also the ammunition used by the service, storage, movement and loading, and repair and inspection as required, unlike in the RAOC whose tradesmen are not concerned with the weapons that use the stores they hold. At the end of this training and 'apprenticeship' the student is a junior technician, similar to the Army lance corporal.

To progress to EOD and IEDD work is more difficult. A tradesman might never have to become involved; none will be called upon to make the dreadful choice, to go active or leave the service. Selection for specialist EOD training is undertaken by the Personnel Branch at RAF Innsworth. All ranks attend courses at the Defence EOD School before becoming part of a station EOD team. They may also attend the airfield clearance course at the RAF school at Wittering.

At time of writing, the Defence EOD School Officers' and Senior NCOs' Advanced EOD Course is of seven weeks' duration, likely to extend to eight to meet the new and complex demands of modern weaponry from all over the world. The course includes two weeks covering the specialist requirement for transition to war, and War Improvised Explosive Device Disposal. There is also a further separate and specialist course at DEODS which covers all aspects of digging and deep recovery of aircraft bombs.

Royal Air Force personnel attend an introductory one-week course at the school in Essex, together with men from the Royal Navy and Royal Engineers. This introduces them to the dreadful terrorist devices. If successful, students then pass on to the Royal Army Ordnance (now the Royal Logistic) Corps School for the various types of training which qualifies them as No.1s, with their own teams. Although there are a number of active IEDD operators in the RAF, very few weapons technicians will be called upon to perform this duty, and never in Northern Ireland. So far as the training courses and numbers trained each year are concerned, around 50 to 60 airmen attend the basic bomb disposal course and possibly ten to fifteen the various courses on IEDD.

The Royal Air Force operates its own specialist EOD training school at Wittering, a part of the aptly named EOD Squadron RAF, within which are three flights, an Airfield EOD research and development team, the EOD operational flight responsible for range clearance that falls within the services brief, and the EOD training school which trains Royal Air Force personnel in all aspects of airfield clearance. This specialist unit is similar to 33 Engineer Regiment (EOD), although slightly smaller in size, with around 100 personnel of all ranks. Although primarily an RAF training school, they also train members of the other services, as may be required.

A trade qualification badge is in use within the service, to indicate that a person is a 'bomb disposal' expert, a pale blue wreath surrounding a pale blue bomb and the letters BD. However, the only people permitted to wear this badge are those graduates of the schools at Wittering and Essex and then only by airmen below the rank of warrant officer. However, as all take very considerable pride in their association with the work, once the training has been completed the badge can be seen, worn unofficially, in many places and on many sleeves including those of senior officers. Perhaps it is time to permit its display by all those entitled to wear it, just like parachutist's or pilot's wings.

It is not possible to serve permanently in an EOD role in the RAF. Apart from the restrictions this would place on promotion prospects, there is a view that familiarity breeds contempt. At present there is only one warrant officer and a few flight sergeants and sergeants on permanent duty, but there are hundreds more fully qualified, who undertake continuation training, and are available should the need arise.

Perhaps it is appropriate to include a reference in this section to the aftermath of the Gulf War, mainly because the contribution was supplied by a member of the RAF, and a member of the UK EOD Team headed by Lieutenant Colonel M. H. H. Brooke OBE of the Royal Engineers, which included RE, RAOC and RAF EOD staff.

The main problem in Kuwait, after the end of the war, was the sheer volume of explosive ordnance on the ground. It has been estimated that the Iraqis had well over two million anti-tank and anti-personnel mines. In addition, there were hundreds of thousands of tons of small arms, mortar and artillery ammunition, demolition explosives and aircraft bombs, all left behind in their rush to depart from Kuwait. Furthermore, there were tens of thousands of bombs and bomblets dropped by the coalition forces, many of which had failed to explode. A survey had to be carried out to plot the location of all these items, to enable their safe disposal.

This was a major task for everyone involved. Years of training and experience were put to the test. During the Second World War explosive ordnance disposal had been made more difficult by the use of booby-traps built into bombs and mines but, fortunately, this was not a problem in the Gulf. Information on all the explosive ordnance used was readily available, even though the Iraqis' stores were mostly of US, French or Soviet manufacture.

An unusual part of the team's work was to produce leaflets in an attempt to dissuade people from collecting, or even touching, the vast quantity of ordnance still lying around. Some 70 servicemen from all nations died after hostilities ceased, and Kuwaiti civilians also died, mainly children. Sergeant Rogers, RAF, was awarded the George Medal for his quick and selfless rescue of two young boys from a coastal minefield. Both boys were seriously injured, with badly damaged legs and but for Sergeant Rogers would undoubtedly have died.

It is on record that this was a period of great frustration for, despite the publicity, people continued to die or be seriously maimed. The Kuwaiti Government was aware of the problem and in an effort to stop people collecting munitions they employed bands of unskilled, cheap labour to drive around the city in large lorries, collecting up what was lying around. It was during one of these collection sprees that a lorry loaded with an estimated ten tons of assorted ammunition caught fire in the car park adjacent to a United Nations Headquarters building, and then exploded. It was unofficially recorded that one of the officers was on the telephone when the 'attack' occurred. He believed that the Iraqis had invaded when a rocket whizzed through his office! Ten tons of assorted munitions can create an amazing scene, and most fortunately no-one was killed or even seriously injured. [*Author's note:* My contributor did admit that his vehicle had been parked next to the lorry, and had disappeared from the face of the earth. I suppose he was forced to report that he had mislaid it.]

The temptation for the coalition forces to recover ammunition for re-use was considerable. However, they had overlooked the effects of the dramatic changes in temperature. Daytime highs of over 55°C caused expansion of the metal casings and the explosive contents were oozing out past the fuzes. At night, when the cases contracted, the explosives in the screw threads were crushed. It only takes one shell in a stack to set off the entire dump. These incidents continued for some months and, in some locations, involved tens of thousands of tons of explosive ordnance. This was 'accidental disposal' on a grand scale!

The customary black humour of those involved with dangerous tasks is recounted by an RAF expert from Kuwait. He was called to attend a fire on an armoured personnel carrier, believed to have a full load of ammunition on board. Arriving at the scene he found that the carrier was actually on a low loader, and that it was this vehicle which had been on fire. All seemed well so he duly departed back to base. Some time later he was asked 'Where was the driver'?' He replied that the driver was all right and in control of the scene. 'Not the driver of the low loader, you fool. The driver of the carrier!' It appeared that the poor soldier had been asleep inside his vehicle. When he awoke and realised that there was a fire he had leaped out of his vehicle but regrettably it was parked on a bridge over another road. He fell a considerable distance, was rendered unconscious and taken to hospital in the belief that he had been the victim of a road accident. He had been temporarily lost.

Another incident involved a bomb which had passed through the wall of a house, in a rather select area. It had travelled in through one wall, through the floor, out at the other side and become buried in the patio. An expert was called in to deal with it after the area had been evacuated. All went well until he became aware that a crowd of interested onlookers had gathered. The evacuation had not actually occurred!

In a more serious vein, the Gulf conflict gave the RAF an opportunity to examine the Allies' explosive ordnance that had failed to function as designed when used in a combat role. No doubt that very valuable practical experience was gained to result in the modification of basic designs, in order further to improve the efficiency of the service.

The military EOD involvement in Kuwait was completed by July 1991, and the remaining clearance work was undertaken by civilian contractors.

Members of the Royal Air Force have been awarded seven George Crosses and seventeen George Medals during the period from 1940 to 1992.

CHAPTER 14

TERRORISM, THE POLICE AND FORENSICS

For as long as explosives have been available and in use, someone in the services has had to dispose of those that failed to function or have come to the end of their useful life. Similarly, terrorists under one guise or another have existed for centuries. Guy Fawkes was actually a terrorist. Today, a terrorist can be defined as someone who is prepared to use any means to gain political aims and recognition. In the eyes of some, terrorists can be freedom fighters, but for the victim, whether friend or foe, the result can be maiming or death with property and livelihood damaged or destroyed – all for a possibly vague political ambition.

Whether an incident involves the Fenians of the later part of the nineteenth century, or the IRA in Coventry in 1939, or the dreadful Birmingham and London bombings of more recent years, whenever terrorists or extremists are in action, someone must be present to try and neutralise the device. It is a simple fact of life that a device must be made safe. Apart from damage to property and person, it is vital to take it to bits to see how it works in order to gain experience for the future. In the early days of the 1970 IRA campaign triggers were used in bombs similar to those used in the 1930s and even earlier.

The subtleties of the terrorist and freedom fighter matter little to the man who gets blown up, and who probably has little interest in their political aims and ambitions. What has been achieved in Northern Ireland over the past century? Very little apart from creating the most experienced anti-terrorist techniques anywhere in the world, and medical facilities highly competent in dealing with the human consequences of the terrorists' actions. The terrorist of today enjoys international co-operation, an exchange of technical information and the supply of equipment and explosives, but so also do those who combat the terrorist. Today there is a far greater degree of co-operation and information. If a source or supply is discovered all those who need to know will be rapidly told. If a new device is discovered, again the word is spread. Thus the fight continues and will be won.

What is a terrorist bomb, or as the professionals refer to it 'Improvised Explosive Device'? It can be anything in size, technical content, sophistication or simplicity. The original anarchist of old has been well depicted carrying a black sphere with a fuze sticking out of the top spitting sparks, the bomb case painted black and, to avoid confusion, the word BOMB is clearly painted on it in white. Regrettably skills and attitudes change, not many bombers these days slink around in black cloaks, with the device held aloft.

The major changes really started during the Second World War. The Allies were intent on causing as much chaos as possible behind enemy lines. In Europe all sorts of strange devices were created by the Special Operations Executive and similar agencies. The difference between neat little piles of what looked like dog muck or even a cow pat might only be discovered when standing on it. One lot smelt awful, the other made you forget all about nasty odours! However as already mentioned there is a subtle difference between mass produced and home made devices. One has the full approval of the state, and is carefully manufactured to a high specification and is usually safe to handle. The other frequently kills the manufacturer during production, or the individual who has the job of placing it in a predetermined location.

Safety devices are often as simple as clothes pegs (wooden type) and being simple, once removed can result in an early catastrophe.

Although all bombers expect the device to be triggered according to plan, many, and particularly in the past 50 years or so, accept that at times someone might be lucky enough to spot the bomb before it explodes, and bright enough to call in the experts. So if they fit additional 'anti-handling mechanisms', they might still succeed. The number and variety of these booby-traps is as endless as a child's imagination: tremblers, light sensitive cells, anti-lift, anti-pull, mercury tilt, you name it someone, somewhere will have used it. The only good news is that the more difficult a bomber makes his device the more likely it is to blow up before its time, and in the wrong place. So far as Northern Ireland is concerned well over 100 'manufacturers' have met an early and untimely very messy end. Regrettably these accidents aren't well publicised or perhaps this would deter continued recruitment.

In order to better understand exactly what is undertaken by those involved with Explosive Ordnance Disposal, be it conventional manufactured items or those devices produced by the terrorist, perhaps a few comments on the chemistry involved is required. An explosive compound is basically a substance that when activated undergoes a rapid change in structure that results in the production of gases and heat. The greater the volume of gas produced, and the greater the heat generated then the greater the power of the explosive. In order to start the cycle the explosive requires a device to commence the chemical change; this trigger is the detonator.

Most explosives are stable, can be hit, dropped or even shot. Some do tend to decompose if stored in unsuitable climates or locations. The detonators are the key to the chain reactions, small very sensitive tubes about the diameter of a pencil and a couple of inches in length. Although terrorists can produce home made explosives they cannot normally produce the detonator.

The basic difference between a high explosive and a low explosive is that the former requires a detonator to start the cycle, whilst the latter does not. Gunpowder is the most common low explosive which can actually be lit with a match. It is not only high explosives that are lethal. If any are restricted by means of a case then the generation of gases from the chemical reaction can be just as effective if someone is near at hand. There are examples of car bombs in Northern Ireland containing thousands of pounds of home made 'low' explosives. All will have seen the blast damage to property on television and seen the remains of the delivery vehicle, the odd wheel and bit of engine. The difference if a high explosive had been used to achieve the same result is only in the quantity. Instead of thousands of pounds only a few pounds would have been needed.

The process of an explosion is the production of a shock wave which creates a pressure front. It is this pressure that causes bodily damage. An over-pressure as low as five to eight pounds will damage the ear-drums, ten to fifteen pounds causes the lungs to collapse. Pressure waves enter the mouth, nose and any other orifice and disrupt the body from the inside; limbs are torn off, flesh can be stripped off the bone, all in a fraction of a second. Even small quantities of explosives can result in shock waves that can inflict the most terrible injuries to the human body. Respect is the order of the day and the greatest respect must be given to terrorist devices no matter how small they may be. Derrick Patrick recounts his examination of the results of a bomb that went off early and destroyed the terrorists who were about to set it in place. A particularly descriptive passage recounts that 'the welter of small pieces of flesh and clothing in one particular spot made it abundantly clear that one bomber at least has been "strained" through the chain link fence, just as if he had been put through a mincing machine'.

The Police

In the majority of incidents on mainland UK, as occurred in Cyprus, Hong Kong, Malaya and all other areas under threat, the first person to attend is a policeman. For many years a very close degree of co-operation has existed between the police and the military authorities. The police are invited to witness the effects of explosives, from small quantities contained in letter bombs to spectacular car bombs. This is not just a good day out, but the real way to get the message across. Bombs are designed to kill, so to understand them one must see the flash, hear the bang and feel the blast in what can be called hands on experience.

To supplement these demonstrations regular joint military and police bomb disposal exercises are conducted. The prime aim of these is the relicensing of EOD personnel but the important secondary aim is exercising the police in dealing with Improvised Explosive Devices, ensuring that their standard operating procedures and personnel are regularly exercised and training is kept up to date. These exercises endeavour to replicate actual incidents but with a greatly condensed time scale. They run from the initial 999 call to the EOD team declaring the area clear, several times a day to ensure all know what to do. Examples of the types of incidents that might be included during one of these exercises are simple letter bombs, suspicious parcels, children playing with explosives, car bombs, to sophisticated hostage situations where explosives are involved. Actors from the military are used and really perform like professionals. They can be aggrieved or injured people, even terrorists and criminals and they try and live up to the part. They might volunteer information or show realistic terror at their predicament, making the situation as real as possible.

The response and actions by the police team are carefully noted by umpires throughout each exercise. They are expected to perform as they would on the streets of their home town. So now anyone having to phone the police can remember that they have been carefully trained and these days will not poke about to see what is in the bag. None of the provincial forces in the UK have their own police bomb squads. Frankly they would be seldom used and adequate cover is readily available throughout the country from RAOC, now RLC, teams. Although some retired military personnel have joined the police as a better paid job than the Army, some even having active service experience, they are not expected to don the bomb suit as policemen.

The training of the regional police forces differs in relation to their size and from previous incidents within their area. Following the Brighton bombing incident in 1985, a greatly improved training pattern was established. Some police officers are sent on special three-week courses, which concentrate on search procedures. One large provincial force has only had a handful of incidents over the past twenty years but sends officers on the regular training exercises and trains approximately 200 men a year in the specialist procedures.

The exception to the rule is London. The Metropolitan Police have their own civilian explosives experts. Regrettably a nation's capital is always the main target for the terrorist. It is usually the centre of government, industry and commerce and as such a ready-made target. London repeatedly features in the news with incidents of a major type. The anti-terrorist branch of Scotland Yard now includes a number of bomb disposal experts. Originally a detachment from the RAOC was based in London under the direction of the Anti-Terrorist Squad; however, it soon became apparent that the 'Met' needed its own personnel. Not only was there the threat from the IRA and all its various offshoots, but also a considerable number of other terrorist groups such as the PLO and those from Europe, and extremist special interest groups, like the animal rights movement, which has taken to planting its own home-made bombs. The need had to be recognised and very quickly men were recruited from the RAOC. All had to be experienced ammunition technicians with hands-on practical experience with the real thing.

During the period from 1970 to 1986, there have been approximately 63,000 bomb alerts in mainland Britain. Obviously many have been false alarms and many have been hoaxes, but a considerable number have been the real thing, and a very large proportion have been in London. A telephone box just yards from Downing Street was one target. The spectators, at a very safe distance, watched and waited as the explosives officer worked with calmness and precision for three hours in the cramped conditions inside the telephone box until the device was made safe. It was later announced on television that a terrorist device, containing five pounds of Semtex, had been made safe near to Downing Street. No panic. No excitement by the expert, just a routine job tackled and completed with care, precision and skill; just another part of his day's work.

These men at the 'Met' are unknown to the general public. Very occasionally the name of one is announced in the Press, not when an award for bravery is made, but when they are killed in action. So it was for Kenneth Howarth in 1981, killed instantly when dealing with a device at a Wimpy Bar in Oxford Street. For this supreme bravery and sacrifice, he was awarded a posthumous George Medal in 1983.

Roger Philips-Goad, who had been awarded the British Empire Medal for gallantry in dealing with terrorist devices in Cyprus in 1958, was killed whilst dealing with a suspect package in the doorway of a shoe shop in Kensington. Having ensured the area was clear, he then approached the device. He was posthumously awarded the highest award for bravery not in the face of the enemy, the George Cross.

Among their peers and colleagues these men, not only in the Metropolitan Police or the Royal Army Ordnance Corps, but all who deal with Improvised Explosive Devices are remembered with a deep feeling. The trade has only had a limited membership over the past 40 years. Most know one another or have friends and colleagues in common. Among themselves they will readily exchange information and this also extends for some on an international scale. They do not talk about the danger but they do talk about the associated problems and inconveniences, working down sewers, under floors or up on roofs. Anyone privileged to meet a group of them, will probably realise that they are normally a nice sociable crowd, good company who seldom reveal what they get up to. In a small group of two or three the odd comment might be picked up. They probably have a somewhat strange sense of humour – who wouldn't in this job?

There is the story of the man who was obsessed with clockwork timing devices; a couple of ticks and he could tell you if it was a Timex or a Smith's. When getting dressed up in the full body armour the last thing the operator puts on is the helmet. When this is on they tap him on the head like a deep-sea diver and off he goes. This poor chap had an alarm clock stuck to the top of his helmet. He took one or two paces, paused and exclaimed over the radio, 'Christ, I can hear the bloody thing ticking from here.' Needless to say once the clock was removed he was sent off to deal with the device. A lesser soul would probably have set off home at once for a bit of peace and quiet.

Some years ago there was a Middle Eastern gentleman who sent his pregnant girlfriend to board a plane. Unknown to her there was a bomb in her luggage. Providentially she was intercepted by the police and her boyfriend was arrested, tried and eventually convicted at the Old Bailey. The device was triggered by a new type of electronic timer and only by running it to destruction (after removing it from the bomb) could the forensic scientist determine the exact time it was set to explode. It would have gone off over the sea and those on the aircraft not killed by the blast or the crash would have drowned. A very major tragedy had been avoided. Now to the point of the story. When the individual was sentenced to 45 years he was seen to smile, when later his legal counsel commented that he was sorry for such a long sentence, the poor chap replied 'Why?, it's only four to five years.' As a foreigner, he had obviously missed a vital part of what was said and when told of the proper sentence legend has it he fell to the floor in a faint. Let us hope the story is true.

As explained earlier in this book, all those involved in the trade are subject to very rigorous selection. Those who have qualified and who have been licensed to deal with terrorist devices are a special breed of person. Those who retire from the Army and continue to work dealing with these devices are even more of a special breed. Although the largest proportion of devices they have to walk up to are hoaxes, or just suspicious packages, the tension is the same. Imagine this as a job, eight-hour shifts around the clock, seven days a week. Even when off duty an operator can be called back in a major emergency.

A retired brigadier and a lieutenant colonel, who had started their own security business, were having a quiet dinner at an Indian restaurant in London. Their conversation, as usual, concerned bombs, equipment and incidents. To their surprise instead of dessert they were served with the Metropolitan Police. The poor old waiter had overheard their conversation and thought that they were terrorists! Even in retirement care has to be taken. As frequently discovered during the Second World War, careless talk costs lives. Armed response teams can give one terrible indigestion, especially when spreadeagled on the floor, as would happen today.

An incident which indicated increased public awareness on the mainland concerned a warrant officer attached to one of the regional EOD Units trying to find accommodation convenient to his base. His Irish accent alerted the prospective landlord and, whilst carrying out his fourth or fifth visit the warrant officer was picked up by the police as a suspected terrorist. It transpired that everyone had telephoned in to report his presence in the area. There were a few red faces, but really better to be safe than sorry.

Just outside the Lancashire town of Ramsbottom is Holcombe Moor Training Camp. It is a desolate place at the best of times, but on 22 January 1975 it was also the scene of a terrible tragedy, the untimely death of an ammunition technician. Following the spate of bombings in 1974, which included incidents at the Tower of London, Guildford, the infamous Birmingham pub bombings and the M62 bus bombs, there was a growing awareness that within the judiciary there existed no knowledge of the effects of exploding devices and, accordingly, it was decided that it would be beneficial for a group of judges and leading counsel to attend a demonstration. This was particularly relevant at the time as those invited to attend were involved with a trial in Manchester, concerning the two Gillespie sisters who were accused of placing incendiary devices at both Debenham's and Lewis's department stores in the city during 1974.

On the day of the demonstration the weather was windy, cold and miserable, the heavy rain seemed to be parallel to the ground. In charge of the demonstration was an RAOC Ammunition Technical Officer, assisted by Staff Sergeant Graham Crawshaw, an experienced Ammunition Technician. In the demonstration it was planned to initiate a number of different types of explosive devices, to demonstrate clearly the awesome effects of explosives and make it plain how relatively small quantities can cause considerable damage. Additionally, it was intended to show that the terrorist used different types of explosives and timing controls in order to achieve different results. Some four or five devices had already been successfully initiated with spectacular results, which had duly impressed the members of the police and legal professions attending the demonstration.

Staff Sergeant Crawshaw was working alone, in the back compartment of a long wheelbase Land-Rover, preparing another device which consisted of plastic explosive with an alarm clock timer control. On the front seat of the vehicle was a German shepherd dog (either his or his officer's mascot). Suddenly, whilst working on the device, there was a massive explosion. My correspondent, who was a police sergeant in Special Branch, very clearly recalls the Land-Rover becoming enveloped in a great orange ball of fire with, to quote his words, 'maroon and other explosions firing from the debris.' The entire incident was watched in numbed silence by those in attendance. Fortunately, incidents of this type are very rare, but those present will never forget what took place that day. A single moment in time, seeming endless, will be etched in their memories forever.

My correspondent, a highly experienced detective sergeant from Special Branch, together with a colleague, had a further traumatic task. Over the following two days they had to collect together the remains of Staff Sergeant Crawshaw. Such was the effect on his memory that he can clearly recall that one part of the body was located 183 yards from the scene of the explosion. The German shepherd, asleep on the front seat, was killed instantly, but its body remained intact. The police officer in charge of this dreadful incident is now an assistant chief constable, and my friend is a detective superintendent. Neither will ever forget that day, 22 January 1975. Probably the greatest irony was that this demonstration was intended to increase an awareness and knowledge in leading counsel who, for whatever reason, had failed to turn up, though the demonstration was viewed by an assortment of judges and senior police officers.

The experience of the 1970s, and this incident, greatly influenced future proceedings. An accident of this type is highly unlikely to occur in the future, although those who deal with explosives know that, even when all standard operating procedures are complied with, sometimes fate can take a hand.

Forensics and the Terrorist

There are a number of organisations involved in dealing with terrorists and explosive devices. As would be reasonable to expect, they are the police, the intelligence agencies and counter-terrorist organisations. Their main task is to stop the terrorist before he can infiltrate his target and complete his specific task. To enable these organisations to succeed they must build up a complete picture of each terrorist organisation not only of its membership, active and passive, but also its aims and objectives and how it plans to succeed, how it is financed, who its donors are and, most important, how it obtains its weapons and explosives and who constructs the bombs. For obvious security reasons it is undesirable to go into detail, but such are the skills, experience and resources of the counter-terrorism agencies, it is likely that most subversive organisations all over the world, and in particular in the UK, are well documented and their explosives experts and their capabilities are well known to those who are required to deal with them.

As well as the NATO information centre already mentioned, a similar international exchange of information takes place about the terrorists, and in particular the 'bomb'. Any new technical improvements, detonating systems, timers or other sophisticated modifications are carefully monitored and the information passed to those who need to know around the world.

An important contribution to this intelligence network is made by the personnel of the Bomb Squad, highly trained technicians from all services, and in particular the Ammunition Technical Officers of the Royal Army Ordnance Corps, now the Royal Logistics Corps, themselves. They have accumulated technical knowledge, which has been carefully documented over many years, provided by others and built up from their own experience from dealing with devices found and rendered safe all over the world.

The reader will admit that art experts and those in the antique-trade can identify paintings, furniture and other works; and with reasonable certainty credit the work to a particular artist or craftsman. So it is with explosive devices. Those rendered safe are carefully examined by the forensic scientist for the type of explosive, what safety devices have been built in, what anti-handling or other booby-traps have been used. The type of components, the wires, batteries and sticky tape all tell a tale, even down to the type of wire-cutters used. It is possible to identify cuts in the wire and confirm that a particular wire-cutter was used. Many of the bomb makers used by the IRA have been at their job for some time; after constructing a number of devices their technique becomes their trade mark. Compared with the average citizen the death rate amongst the bomb manufacturers is rather high. They have to use whatever materials are available to them and often these are of a dangerous and unstable quality. Few ever retire to an old age in a rose-covered country cottage.

The real job of modern bomb forensics is to gather all the evidence from the scene of the explosion. Every last scrap, fragment and damaged item has to be painstakingly collected together and its precise location in relation to the scene of the explosion noted. Television frequently records lines of policemen on hands and knees carefully going over the scene of an explosion. This is what it is all about. They start work as soon as the Explosive Ordnance Disposal team has confirmed that the area is clear of any secondary devices and spend as long as is necessary to thoroughly search the area. If it is a confined space this can be for a short time; if it is a large bomb in an open space the area to be searched can be considerable and the job will take much longer. The reader should imagine being on his or her hands and knees, in the rain, fed up, soaked to the skin, knowing there are hours to go – no 'nine-to-five' routine, just grit the teeth and get on with the job.

Another matter which receives little publicity for obvious reasons is the effect on the victims of the device. Before their remains can be removed they must be photographed and examined at the scene. Even these tragic remains have a story to tell. In the incident already recounted in which a device exploded prematurely and killed those who were arming it prior to placing it into position, it was only by a close examination of their remains that it was apparent from the number of vertebrae that three and not two, as originally had been believed, had died. Some of the pieces had been spread over a very considerable distance. Gory and very unpleasant though this is, someone has this job to do. After every incident that involves people as victims, some poor soul has the job of collecting up the debris. The odd arm or leg cannot just be left lying around. A medical examiner provides detailed autopsy and tissue deformation information to the forensic scientist. This information is vital in identifying the type and strength of the explosive used, and sometimes parts of the device itself can be recovered from the body.

As already stated, the forensic collection teams inspect the entire area, identify all fragments and debris. These are then photographed in situ and marked. The centre of the blast has to be established, although this is not usually too difficult. The entire site is then photographed and a detailed scale plan is prepared. The location of every item recovered is then recorded. The results of this painstaking work provide considerable information to the experts. The timing device which is at the centre of the explosion is often recovered virtually intact. It is amazing what information this can provide. Some watch repairers mark the inside of the case when it is repaired, giving clues as to previous owners, although this method of delay is used less frequently in today's high-tech world.

The type of explosive used is readily identified and once the explosive is known it is possible to calculate the amount used with a high degree of accuracy. Some explosives contain trace particles mixed into them during manufacture as an aid to identification, some of the home-made varieties do not totally disintegrate and traces of the compound can be found. If the explosives have been contained in a box, suitcase or similar object then those pieces are collected together and like a jigsaw reassembled. Perhaps the odd fingerprint remains, or even the original owner's name and address, from what might have been one of the terrorist's own old suitcases. Stranger things do happen in real life.

The focal point of the explosion is probably the richest for the forensic scientist. Here can be found fragments of the packaging, particles of the explosive, wire used to manufacture the device, perhaps electronic components, timing circuit boards, parts of the detonator, dry cell batteries, relays, and anti-handling components. All are capable of telling the expert a very interesting story.

The laboratory personnel examine pieces of metal. After an explosion the heat melts the outer edge of fractured metal; when it cools, there is a gas wash on the edge. This can be analysed and can provide information on the velocity of the detonation and the type and quantity of explosive used. Fragments recovered from human remains pass to the expert who assesses the location of the victim and depth of penetration of the fragments, which provides essential information to build up the picture.

The process of building up the picture only takes a few days; initial reactions based on years of experience are available within hours. Most bombs are either preceded or followed by claims by various groups responsible for the act. Forensic science can prove who did the dreadful deed and often provide sufficient information to identify the manufacturer and his colleagues. This information is relayed to others within the security service who can act to prevent other targets being destroyed and take steps to detain the perpetrators for trial. The forensic evidence so painstakingly collected will be used at the trial to ensure conviction.

This science is ever improving the expertise of all those involved and often traces the design of anti-handling and other booby-traps that would have killed an unsuspecting explosives officer. The goal of forensic science is not only the conviction of those involved but the improvement of technology and understanding to aid detection and prevention and the final end of these dreadful acts.

CHAPTER 15

SELF-PROTECTION: A GUIDE

The growth of incidents on the British mainland continues. Frequently these take the form of small incendiary devices, sometimes letter bombs; but sometimes of larger devices intended to cause chaos and devastation in London, on the Underground, a main line station, or a city centre. This growth has produced its own problem when the public have tried to help. 'Why is that bomb in a bucket of water?' enquires the technician. 'Oh, I thought it would put the fuze out', replies the public-spirited lunatic. It is worth remembering that these devices are designed to kill. Once laid they may have a built in anti-handling device and so –

Don't touch it – call the police. Very few of them will touch it, either. There was an incident in Manchester some years ago. A holdall was discovered on the steps of the new courthouse. The area was cleared and the Bomb Squad was called. Whilst waiting for them to arrive, the Superintendent of Police wandered up to the device and gave it a little prod with his baton, then, to his horror, he realised that it was a bomb. He turned and ran and had just got out of range when it exploded. The blast knocked him over but didn't damage anything more than his pride. You've heard about the Flying Doctor? He is known as the Flying Policeman.

Following a recent outbreak of small incendiary devices planted in shops in the north of England, an area Police Authority has taken the trouble to prepare a leaflet of general advice which is summarised as follows:

- Do not be complacent, look at your own security and take simple precautions.
- A bomb is not round and black with a sign saying 'Bomb'.
  It can look like a book or a music cassette, it can be in a brief case or lady's handbag or even a packet of cigarettes.

There are a number of general precautions that you can take. Following the Baltic Exchange bomb in London, the Association of British Insurers have produced two short training videos with booklets which clearly show what can be done to minimise personal risk.

Take basic security precautions, keep doors and windows locked whenever possible, do not leave rubbish lying around outside. A bomb can easily be hidden and never noticed. If a terrorist campaign is in effect then be extra vigilant, perhaps instituting a security check on handbags or carrier bags. A terrorist is unlikely to gain entry when there is a risk of a search. He will choose a softer target. Always check the premises at the close of business to ensure that no unidentifiable article is lying around. Train your staff to be aware. Even in the most chaotic or cluttered shop people can be aware of the unusual if trained to look and watch. Two examples come to mind. A shopkeeper returned from lunch and noticed that a baby's pram had been sold – congratulations to his young staff! What had actually occurred was that a couple of shoplifters with a baby had walked in, put the baby in the pram and walked out. He had spotted the space immediately. Another shopkeeper returned to his shop and immediately noticed a number of items were missing; on enquiry he found out that they had not been sold but had been stolen. Both of these individuals would also notice any package left behind and out of the ordinary. If they can do this so can you. Watch what people do, if a terrorist feels watched he will move on.

The purpose of a 'bomb' is to cause chaos, so when a campaign starts it usually includes a few live ones and a host of hoaxes. If you get a telephone call take it very seriously, prepare a report form for your telephone reception staff, which must be simple yet concise, and must contain as much information as possible about the caller.

- Man, woman, child – young or old?
- Intoxicated, rambling or confident, speech impediment?
- Laughing, serious, hesitant, nervous?
- Accent?
- Was the message read out or spontaneous?
- Write down the message.
- Any noise on the line, call box, any tones on the line, car phone, operator interruptions, anyone else in the background?
- Any background noise – traffic, talking, music, typing, machinery, aircraft or trains?
- Note the time of the call and the person who received it.

If you receive a bomb threat then you must treat is as real. *Do not* put down the 'phone, but obtain as much information as possible. Say that it's a bad line and get the caller to repeat the message whilst you write it down, in particular ask about the following:

- Where is it?
- What time will it go off?
- What does it look like?
- What type of bomb is it? (type of explosive such as Semtex)
- Why are you doing this?
- Who are you? (what organisation)

When the call is over instruct the employee to call a senior person at once. Don't laugh it off. Telephone the police. They will take it very seriously. If you have been told where the bomb is then don't go and have a look – evacuate the area. It is better to look a bit foolish than to be dead.

There are a number of bombs currently in use by the terrorist:

High Explosive Blast Bombs designed to kill and cause maximum damage. These are usually controlled by a timing device and are often fitted with an anti-handling booby-trap mechanism. They can be as small as a packet of cigarettes or as large as a holdall. If you believe that you have one on your premises *do not touch it,* telephone the police and clear the premises.

Incendiary Devices designed to produce intense heat and quickly set fire to the surrounding area. These are usually very small (music cassettes or cigarette packets are ideal containers), hidden in pockets on displayed clothing or behind other goods on shelves. Search your premises each day, train your staff to watch the customers. Whatever you do, *don't touch them*; if the timer has reached its end you would undoubtedly get severely burned.

Letter Bombs. These can contain either high explosive or incendiary devices. Just because they are only a quarter of an inch thick does not mean that there is insufficient explosive content to kill you and destroy your office. Take care. Are you a potential target? Look for the following:

- Grease marks on the envelope.
- A smell of marzipan or almonds.
- Visible wires.
- Does the package feel heavy for its size?

* Is the weight distribution uneven?
* Are the contents rigid?
* Are there too many stamps on it for the weight? Has it been posted outside Great Britain?

Finally, if you have to call the police and if they in turn have to call out the Bomb Squad, they both have a set procedure. Perhaps if the reader is aware of some of the questions which will be asked by the technician it might save time in helping him render the device safe, and save your property from extensive damage.

* Where is it?
* What safety precautions have you taken?
* What is it? (as detailed a description as possible)
* What size is it?
* How long has it been there?
* Has it been moved?
* How long has it been under observation and by whom?
* What other hazards are in the vicinity? LPG tanks, bulk paint, petrol storage, gas main, flammable chemicals, etc.

You will be asked these questions by the police, probably several times, and most probably by the bomb disposal team as soon as they arrive. Try not to panic. Remember, this is unlikely ever to happen to you, but if you remain calm all will be well.

CHAPTER 16

ONE HUNDRED YEARS ON: THE FINAL SUMMARY

The original intention of this book was to record the history of Explosive Ordnance Disposal in the Royal Army Ordnance Corps, from its beginning, in 1896, until its demise, in 1993. However, the record has been taken further in time to 1996, in order to cover the first century. What changes have we seen over those years? In some ways, not many. No doubt the Laboratory Foreman of 1896 would be a welcome member of the sergeants' mess of today, and would be able to hold his own with an Ammunition Technician member, perhaps not technically, but in all other ways known so well by the 'old and bold'.

From the Army Ordnance Corps of 1896, to the Royal Army Ordnance Corps of 1918, to the Royal Logistics Corps of 1993 two further major changes have occurred. The Laboratory Foreman in 1896 became the Ammunition Examiner in 1922 and was again renamed as Ammunition Technician in 1961. The badge also underwent three changes, from white wreath on khaki with the letters A E, to the large coloured version of a flaming bomb of the early 1950s, to the present full colour, though rather smaller version, of today (no doubt following the Whitehall masters' doctrine of cost cutting.) However, strangely, the overall numbers of Ammunition Technical Officers and Ammunition Technicians have remained the same for several decades, perhaps as a result of the continuing need for specialist services in places like Northern Ireland.

As the photographs show, the equipment has also changed. The original Wheelbarrow was an incredible device. Mark I was developed in March 1972; by June 1973 it had become Mark V, which led to the Mark VII in 1975, which same model remained in use, with modifications, for the next 20 years. Around 1984 a Mark VIII was developed. With its aluminium chassis it can peer down holes and, by changing stance on its tracks, can lift heavy weights. It is also considerably faster cross country! This machine can be controlled by radio or cable; various booms are available and other 'tools' may be fitted, as the need arises. In order to deal with explosive devices in situations where Wheelbarrow cannot go, the Buckeye was introduced in 1995. Far smaller, it was originally designed for use on aircraft or trains.

During the Second World War, and in the late 1940s, the Ammunition Examiner's kit fitted into a small box. His transport was invariably a 15cwt truck or a 'Tilley' Austin van, though it appears in photographs more of a pick-up with canvas rear roof. Then came the progression through Jeeps and Land-Rovers, until the Northern Ireland conflict with the first Wheelbarrow and a rapid growth in the range of necessary kit. 1974 saw the introduction of the long wheelbase Series 3 Land-Rovers, fitted with ramps and cupboards; in 1976 the Ford Transit vans Mark 1, with GRP Armour; 1978 the Mark 2 Ford Transit; 1982 the Renault Dodge was introduced to handle the ever increasing weights carried; 1987 the Ford Transit Mark 3; 1990 the Sherpa and currently the armoured Leyland Daf and, whilst in Northern Ireland, the Tactica, well over 10 tons when fully laden.

So far as Northern Ireland is concerned, from a high level of 6,786 incidents attended by 321 Company in 1973, to 176 incidents in 1995, the demand for highly trained and dedicated ATOs and ATs continues, despite the reductions in the other armed forces.

Although this book has concentrated on Explosive Ordnance Disposal it has also shown that this is only one part of the work undertaken by Ammunition Technicians. Perhaps the reader has received the message that wherever the British Army travels with its ammunition and explosive stores there also go the ATs. So it is in the former Republic of Yugoslavia. In the winter of 1992, the United Nations Mission, 'Operation Grapple' commenced. A one-battalion battle group was deployed to support the UN, with a requirement of 300 tons of ammunition together with a Captain ATO and junior NCO AT. This was later supplemented by a senior NCO AT. Before long their task was increased by the supply of an additional 800 tons of artillery ammunition. The single ammunition troop was increased to two, as the quantity of ammunition was increased.

Though the problems associated with the receipt, storage and supply of ammunition differed in many ways from those problems experienced in the Falklands and the Gulf, one remains the same – the weather. In summer a temperature of 40°C, with storage containers reaching 20°C greater than the outside air is not really suitable for some mortar ammunition, whilst in winter, the cold (–30°C) and the rain gave problems of their own. Ammunition packing was used to make fires to try to keep warm up on Mount Igman, and wet propelling charges were often seen spread out drying in the sun. Both of these practices had to be addressed.

Today, the ammunition procurement system is such that any consumption routinely takes about four years to replace. The 'we are on operations' excuse is unacceptable and it falls to the ATO to remind unit quartermasters that a realistic approach must be found. This normally comes as a threat from the QM to his troops, and usually works. Troops in a position of imminent conflict do tend to have other matters on their minds than 'best value for money' or the four-year replacement problem!

As time passed 'Operation Grapple' became 'Operation Resolve', though the task of the ATO and AT remained, as before, to ensure that the right ammunition was in the right place at the right time, regardless of all other considerations. In a war-torn environment, with no reasonable facilities and in winter temperatures lower than –30°C, ammunition storage became of far less importance than the survival of the troops. The underlying beliefs that ammunition can look after itself will need to be dispelled in the future. The value of ammunition assets in the theatre of conflict are put at over £100 million. Whatever the politicians eventually decide, the Corps and the ATO and ATs will have to uplift this and return it to the UK, or Germany. This will be one logistic problem in the future.

Every new theatre of conflict produces new logistical problems. Perhaps the current consistent theme is 'cost effectiveness'. However, a nation can hardly be an effective military power and penny pinching at the same time.

Finally, as selection into the trade has again changed, and psychometric testing has moved on from 'in house' by the Army medics to privatisation, to back 'in house' in a modified form – what of the future? When this work began in 1988 the then Director, John Sharland, insisted that there was no place in the trade for a woman. Equality meant that she would have to be sent to Northern Ireland, and would become a target simply because of her sex! Now, some seven years later there are a number of women commissioned ATOs, and also ATs.

Over the past 25 years or so, Post Traumatic Stress Disorder (PTSD) has become recognised by the military. Cases were highlighted in the British Army following the Falklands and the Gulf Wars and are now being attributed to Northern Ireland (perhaps it even occurred in the trenches, during the First World War and before!). Any job that involves prolonged exposure to constant danger and witnessing horrific scenes causing death or injury to others, will produce stress and may induce stress related disorders. Further difficulty is experienced when dealing with high calibre, intelligent, highly trained and self-motivated people who are unlikely to admit to their colleagues that they are suffering from psychological problems. Mental illness is simply not admitted until the blokes in white coats carry one off! Even then, too often, it is all put down to a mistake. A stiff upper lip is all well and good but, after a century of change, perhaps in-depth consideration could produce an acceptable solution to 'suffering in silence'. Post Traumatic Stress Disorder is considered by the people working in this field to be a normal reaction to an unbearable situation, and good de-briefing after traumatic situations can minimise the long term effects.

1996

To mark 25 years of service in Northern Ireland by 321 EOD Squadron various tributes were received. Some of those are reproduced below.

The Prime Minister

The extraordinary skill, dedication and courage which the Squadron have had to display on a daily basis, in the service of the whole community in Northern Ireland, have my highest admiration.

The plain statistics are impressive enough: over 46,000 emergency calls dealt with, some 5,500 bombs made safe, over 200 tonnes of explosives recovered. But the people of Northern Ireland know too the reality behind those statistics: countless lives and livelihoods saved, homes protected from devastation and untold suffering prevented.

Your contribution to the community over 25 years is all the more remarkable for being achieved by a unit whose strength has never been more than 100 soldiers. The remarkable valour of those who have served with the Squadron have made it the most decorated unit in the British Army for actions undertaken in peacetime. Its members have received over 300 gallantry awards.

But the sacrifice has also been great. It is tragic that in saving and protecting others, your small unit suffered so many comrades killed and injured. Many today will think of them and their families. I send my deep appreciation to all who have served with the Squadron over the last 25 years and to their families, together with my very best wishes for the future. — *John Major*

Secretary of State for Defence

In a period when the people of Northern Ireland have suffered some appalling acts of terrorism, the sterling efforts of your unit have saved many lives and much property from destruction. I know that, sadly, this has not been without cost to the Squadron: that it is the most decorated unit in the British Army for actions undertaken in peacetime bears witness to the bravery and dedication of its members. Your professionalism makes a vital contribution to this Government's efforts to counter the terrorist threat in Northern Ireland, and to ensure as far as we are able that the people who live there can go about their daily business without the fear of indiscriminate violence. — *Michael Portillo*

Secretary of State for Northern Ireland

I know I speak for every law-abiding citizen in Northern Ireland when I express my deepest gratitude for the heroism and sacrifice shown by 321 Explosives Ordnance Disposal Squadron over the past 25 years. I recall vividly the television pictures from the 1970s and '80s of the lone Ammunition Technical Officer on a lonely walk towards a cargo of potential death and destruction. That has been a scene repeated time and time again in a terrorist campaign which generated 46,000 emergency calls, almost 6,000 of which involved actual explosive devices.

Since 1972 321 Squadron's roll of honour records twenty officers killed and twenty-four seriously injured while carrying out this difficult and very dangerous duty. Small wonder that soldiers from the unit have received nearly 300 awards for gallantry. This record speaks for itself.

When the Squadron celebrates its 25th anniversary. It will be an occasion to recall with pride the unparalleled achievements of this unit, and to remember those who have given their lives or sustained grievous injury to protect others.

I salute 321 Explosive Ordnance Disposal Squadron on its distinguished record over the past 25 years. — *Sir Patrick Mayhew*

Chief Constable, Royal Ulster Constabulary

It is difficult to find appropriate words to acknowledge the debt which the people of Northern Ireland in general, and the Royal Ulster Constabulary in particular, owe to the members of 321 EOD Squadron. For 25 years your officers have been, often quite literally, the last line of defence for the law abiding people of the Province.

It would clearly be inappropriate to single out any particular acts of courage but it comes as no surprise that 321 EOD Squadron is the most decorated unit in the British Army for actions undertaken in peace time; what a remarkable record! Your officers have saved countless lives and prevented the destruction of property on a vast scale. The price you have paid, however, has been horrendous; twenty of your officers have been killed and twenty-four seriously injured. No organisation is better placed than the Royal Ulster Constabulary to fully appreciate the pain and suffering these casualties have caused and continue to cause for the families and next of kin. As we mark this significant anniversary they, and those who made the supreme sacrifice, must be foremost in our thoughts.

On behalf of every member of the RUC I thank you for your twenty-five years of selfless assistance and look forward to the day when, through your own outstanding effort, your unique skills are no longer required in Northern Ireland. In the meantime, thank God you're here!

The words of John Bunyan in The Pilgrim's Progress are, I feel, totally appropriate –

'Who would true valour see,
Let him come hither ...'

— *Ronnie Flanagan,* Chief Constable, Royal Ulster Constabulary

Chief of the Defence Staff

The Squadron has made a unique and vital contribution to the Security Force's resolve to maintain law and order in the Province.

The impressive list of gallantry awards awarded to the members of the Squadron underlines the risks involved in explosive ordnance disposal. During your anniversary celebrations you will of course be maintaining your vigilance and reflecting on those who gave their lives whilst serving with the Squadron.

The Squadron is held in the highest regard by the Armed Forces and on behalf of them may I congratulate you on 25 years' service. — *Field Marshal Sir Peter Inge GCB*

CHIEF OF THE GENERAL STAFF

On the occasion of the 25th Anniversary of its formation, I am writing to thank 321 Explosive Ordnance Disposal Squadron, Royal Logistic Corps for the quite remarkable work it has done during its existence. Your contribution to maintaining a stable environment in Northern Ireland far outweighs the numbers who have served with the Squadron.

The part played by 321 (EOD) Squadron is reflected in the impressive list of gallantry awards awarded to its members during the Troubles. I know the Squadron is the most decorated unit in the British Army for actions undertaken in peacetime. It is this bravery shown by the Ammunition Technical Officers and their teams which causes the Squadron to be held in the very highest regard by the rest of the British Army.

On behalf of all those who have served in Northern Ireland over the past 25 recent years I wish to thank you for this service. — *General Sir Charles Guthrie GCB LVO OBE ADC Gen*

COMMANDER IN CHIEF

I simply wanted to take this opportunity to write to express my admiration for the enormous contribution that has been made by members of the Squadron over the last 25 years.

You always operated in the most dangerous environment and shown tremendous courage as well as remarkable skill, as a result of which many people's lives have been saved to say nothing of the destruction of property that has been prevented.

As GOC from 1993 until earlier this year, nobody knows better than me just how wonderful your contribution has been to the counter-terrorist campaign. — *General Sir Roger Wheeler KCB CBE*

DIRECTOR GENERAL LOGISTIC SUPPORT (ARMY)

In my position as Director General of the Royal Logistic Corps, I am delighted to be able to congratulate 321 Explosive Ordnance Disposal Squadron, past and present, on achieving 25 years of outstanding service in Northern Ireland. It is only fitting that this anniversary is being recognised both at local and national levels.

Even though the level of violence may have diminished since 1971, the sophistication and skill of the enemy has progressed rapidly, generating an ever increasing threat to you all. The Unit's record of achievement and skill is acknowledged throughout the world and it is impossible to quantify how many lives the skills of your teams have saved and how much collateral damage has been prevented. The recent atrocity in Thiepval Barracks is a timely reminder that we still have a long way to go before a long lasting peace is secured for the Province. — *Major General M S White CBE*

CHAPTER 17

NONE BUT THE BRAVE: GALLANTRY AWARDS 1915–1995

Cold-blooded courage without the excitement of facing an enemy in the heat of battle is probably the hardest form of self discipline that any man can be called upon to exert. The George Cross was instituted by Royal Warrant on 24 September 1940, amended by a new Warrant on 8 May 1941. The George Cross, which may be awarded posthumously, is awarded 'only for the acts of the greatest heroism or the most conspicuous courage in circumstances of extreme danger.' It superseded the Medal of the Order of the British Empire for Gallantry, and any recipient of that medal was required to return it to the Central Chancery of the Orders of Knighthood and to receive the George Cross in its place.

The Cross is intended primarily for civilians throughout the Commonwealth – men and women – and its award to members of the fighting services is confined to actions for which purely military honours are not normally granted. It is perhaps the highest award likely ever to be given to a bomb disposal officer of any service. This is due to the fact that the Victoria Cross may only be awarded for supreme gallantry and sacrifice in the face of the enemy or on a field of battle.

SUPPLEMENT TO THE LONDON GAZETTE

CENTRAL CHANCERY TO THE ORDERS OF KNIGHTHOOD

St James's Palace, SW1

The KING has been graciously pleased to approve the award of the GEORGE CROSS, in recognition of most conspicuous gallantry in carrying out hazardous work in a very brave manner, to the undermentioned:

17 December 1940
Captain Robert Llewellyn Jephson JONES
Lieutenant William Marsden EASTHAM
Royal Army Ordnance Corps

11 October 1946
Temporary Major Kenneth Alfred BIGGS
Acting Staff Sergeant Sidney George ROGERSON
Royal Army Ordnance Corps

The QUEEN has been graciously pleased to approve the award of the GEORGE CROSS, in recognition of most conspicuous gallantry in carrying out hazardous work in a very brave manner, to the undermentioned:

10 January 1972
Major S. G. (George) STYLES
Royal Army Ordnance Corps

November 1990
WO1 (SSM) Barry JOHNSON
Royal Army Ordnance Corps

The great majority of people never see the *London Gazette*, though there may be occasional reports in local newspapers. Few people know what really happened to enable an individual to be even considered for an award for gallantry, let alone actually receive a decoration.

Perhaps the following might go part way to adding a little more background to the acts that resulted in the award of the GEORGE CROSS to the six very gallant members of the Corps.

CAPTAIN ROBERT LLEWELLYN JEPHSON JONES
LIEUTENANT WILLIAM MARSDEN EASTHAM

On various dates these two officers worked under dangerous and trying conditions and performed acts of conspicuous gallantry in dealing with large numbers of various unexploded bombs, some of which were in a highly dangerous state and of the German delayed action type. On one occasion these two officers showed particular gallantry in dealing with a 1,100lb bomb – two attempts were made to explode this bomb but it failed to detonate; at the third attempt, when it was at its most dangerous state, they succeeded in detonating it. On a second occasion these officers, assisted by a Master Rigger from HM Dockyard, succeeded in removing a 400lb unexploded bomb, which had been under water for a week, from a twenty foot deep well inside a house. The bomb was fuzed at both ends and in a dangerous state. It had to be raised to the ground floor by means of a gyn, tackles, slings and rope. The operation was doubly dangerous as there was a possibility of the sling slipping when the bomb was being hauled up, as the bomb was 2ft 6in long and the mouth of the well only 3ft 1inch wide and for safety the bomb had to be kept horizontal.

Lieutenant Eastham, assisted by the Master Rigger, guided the bomb from the floor of the well. Captain Jones went to the top to guide it through the opening and succeeded in getting the bomb out although there was only 6 inches clearance as it came through the mouth of the well.

For their gallant help in dealing with the bomb in the well, Commissioned Boatswain Lord Joseph Herbert Sheldon was awarded the George

Medal and for pumping water from the well and then clearing the mud from around the bomb. Mr Lawrence Thake, a civilian fitter from the Public Works Department, was awarded the George Medal.

TEMPORARY MAJOR KENNETH ALFRED BIGGS
ACTING STAFF SERGEANT SYDNEY GEORGE ROGERSON

At Savernake, Wiltshire, on 2nd January, 1946, during the loading of an ammunition train from lorries, a major explosion occurred and fire broke out, which quickly spread to another ammunition train alongside. Until 16.30hrs further major explosions and extensive fires supervened, involving the death of eight soldiers, injuries to others and the total destruction of twenty-seven railway wagons and two lorries containing shell, mines and other explosives out of a total of ninety-six wagons loaded with ammunition in the sidings.

During a 11/2hr period immediately after the first explosion, as officer in charge, Major Biggs arrived at the scene. With a magnificent disregard for his personal safety, having sized up the situation at once and whilst coolly and determinedly directing operations and completely ignoring the bursting of heavy calibre shell about him, he, amongst other physical work, with another officer, uncoupled and pushed a burning wagon of 5.5 inch shell away from one of the fires and helped to extinguish it. He exorted and inspired all ranks by his superlative leadership in a situation fraught with extreme and intense danger, a contingency, as an ammunition officer, he was more than fully aware of. Major Biggs organised fire breaks in the face of further cordite fire and explosions and his courage and devotion to duty was superb; undoubtedly the work that he did in so magnificent and gallant a manner in the midst of an intense inferno, in which over two hundred tons of explosive either detonated or burnt, throwing destruction over a wide area, was largely instrumental in preventing further disaster.

It is considered that it is due to these officers' exceptionally brave conduct throughout, that local habitations, and probably the town of Marlborough, were spared from devastation. After the third severe explosion at approximately 16.30hrs, when he was floored by a blast, he immediately went forward to reconnoitre and inspected the whole blast area closely, refusing to permit others to accompany him. Having decided that further loss of life might easily occur with other attempts at fire fighting, and deciding that further explosions were remote, he ordered the evacuation of the railhead, being himself the last to leave. He was noticed shortly after this to have the situation fully under control, and that he had done everything in his power that was reasonably possible, despite the strain of such a major incident. He remained on duty and personally observed the fires until they were finally extinguished at mid-day the next day. Major Biggs acted more than fully in accordance with the highest traditions of the British Army.

For the first 11-hour period, when an inferno was raging and further explosions momentarily expected, Staff Sergeant Rogerson, with a total disregard for his personal safety and with a magnificent display of courage and initiative, took complete control of the situation at the siding, with great calmness and efficiency until the arrival of a superior. On his own initiative, he organised fire parties and commenced unloading wagons of ammunition adjacent to and threatened by fire, personally rescued badly wounded men from under blazing ammunition wagons, and helped to organise the removal of injured away from the danger area. His entire conduct was undoubtedly a tremendous inspiration to all around him. By his cool appreciation of the essential situation, he obviously assisted to prevent a far greater disaster and during the whole time, he conducted himself in accordance with the highest possible traditions of the British Army. His courage was of the highest order and even the burning of heavy calibre shells did not deter him from the self-appointed task. Sticking to his post in the face of extreme danger to his life until ordered to withdraw.

This is the cold and somewhat official citation. Perhaps the following extract from the *RAOC Gazette* might add a little bit more colour and realism:

On a bitter cold winter's afternoon with the light beginning to fail in one of England's beauty spots, Savernake Forest, a handful of half frozen men in the RAOC, Pioneer Corps and RASC (Airborne) were completing loading a train with American and German ammunition. In the same siding another loaded British ammunition train was standing, ninety-six wagons in all. Suddenly there was a blinding flash and heavy detonation and two railway wagons and a three-ton lorry literally disappeared. Fire, the terror of all ammunition personnel, swept around the area, more wagons burst into flames and officers and men were galvanised into action. The few actually working on the siding were rapidly reinforced by the Depot Officers and every man near to hand. All were actuated by the fear of the fires spreading to all remaining loaded wagons and subconsciously came the thought of danger to nearby habitation. A thousand tons of explosive was likely to 'go off'.

Working at high pressure, a multiplicity of actions took place in quick succession. Full wagons were uncoupled and pulled out of danger, burning wagons were extinguished, fire breaks were made by manual pushing of the wagons up or down the line, the injured were rescued from under burning wagons and full lorries of ammunition were driven out of harm's way. The force of the original explosion had started fires in wagons yards away. 5.5 inch shell in some of these actually detonated with a tremendous roar, and in doing so, started more fires. Cordite on other wagons 'flashed' again spreading further fire. The darkness which had fallen was intensified by the glare of the burning cartridges and the flash of detonating shell, and to add to the men's difficulties the water tanks soon ran dry, and the water actually froze if far enough away from the heat. Eight men had already been killed and six more injured, but still the others worked in a complete inferno of bursting heavy calibre shell, exploding cartridges and mines. During this period, two more explosions occurred, each of them hurling debris up to a radius of half a mile.

Some five hundred 5.5 inch shells completely detonated or burst in this period and over ten thousand 25 pdr cartridges blazed, pieces of railway wagons, axles, couplings, railway track, anti-tank mines, shell cartridges, timber and concrete rained down continually on the sidings and the adjoining countryside. All in all, twenty-nine railway wagons and their contents exploded. Ten of these wagons completely disappeared and of thirteen more, only the smallest fragments could be found. Of two three-ton lorries only the gear box of one was found. The blast of the explosions was so powerful that a man was lifted two hundred yards by it, landed in a field and got up amazed, but not too badly injured. However, the frantic gallant efforts of the determined few were successful at last. Although the lines were cut at the exit by the first explosion, the full wagons thus bottled-up in the sidings did not catch fire, due to the fire breaks that had been made. The officer in charge, realising that it was impossible to do any more, then ordered complete withdrawal from the sidings and threw a cordon around it to keep watch on the isolated wagons burning themselves out. Parties of men had previously scoured the area hoping to find comrades, stumbling about in the dark over mines, shells and detonators, but to no avail. Had the whole of the wagons gone off, it is impossible to imagine what would have happened to the surrounding countryside; as it was, the blast actually damaged houses some miles away.

In the cold light of dawn the area presented an amazing sight, three wagons were still burning, and were finally extinguished at 11 o'clock. Two huge craters, one seventy feet by thirty feet by fourteen feet deep, and one ninety feet by forty feet by twenty feet deep, resulted from the first and final explosions. The remains of lorries, thousands of 5.5 inch shell, 25 pdr cartridges, anti-tank mines, detonators, packages, telegraph poles, etc. were strewn around like grass seed. How the working party escaped further injury in the midst of this devastation is past comprehension. But true to tradition, to training and British courage, every man continued doggedly at his task acting either on orders or on his own initiative amidst death and destruction ever present in the bursting shell and exploding cartridges. They are ordinary men but of such are heroes made. Even though eight men died that night, but for the efforts of those who remained the loss of life might well have been ten times that number.

Few are honoured, many are not. It is extremely difficult to get British soldiers to talk of their own deeds or even those of others, whether it be an occasion of extreme gravity such as this, or of their own particular prowess in other realms. Those who are honoured receive it not only in their own names but that of others who worked with them.

GEORGE CROSS - Captain (T/Major) Kenneth Alfred BIGGS, RAOC and A/Staff Sergeant Sidney George ROGERSON, RAOC.

GEORGE MEDAL - Sergeant Douglas Arnold KEY, RAOC and Sergeant James Henry MATTHEWS, Pioneer Corps.

[*Author's comment:* Can you imagine how two men could uncouple and physically push a loaded goods wagon, which was actually on fire, away from the main area, and then set about putting out the fire? Perhaps a lifetime's adrenaline was used in the space of a few minutes.]

Major S. G. (George) Styles

As Senior Ammunition Technical Officer, Northern Ireland, Major Styles was responsible for the supervision of the Explosive Ordnance Disposal teams in the Royal Army Ordnance Corps deployed to deal with the ever increasing number of explosive devices used in the terrorist campaign.

On 20th October 1971, Major Styles was called to assist with a device of an apparently new design placed in a public telephone kiosk in Belfast's comparatively new and largest hotel, the Europa. Major Styles immediately went to the scene and having ensured that the military and police had secured the area, and evacuation of personnel had also been effected, took charge of the operation of neutralising, removing and dismantling the bomb. Investigation revealed that the bomb was of a new and complicated construction with anti-handling devices to defeat attempts to disarm it. Until the electrical circuit had been neutralised, the slightest movement could set it off. The device contained between 10 and 15lbs of explosive and could have caused instant death as well as extensive damage. No one was more aware of the destructive capability of the bomb than Major Styles, yet he placed himself at great personal risk to minimise the danger to his team, to confirm the success of each stage of the operation, and to ensure the practicability of the next stage.

A report of the actions that led to this award were recorded in the *RAOC Gazette* in February 1972:

> In September 1969 Major Styles was posted to Northern Ireland to be DADOS with the responsibility for stores and vehicles. He assumed the appointment of Senior Ammunition Technical Officer and General Staff Officer (EOD) in November 1970 when it became apparent that terrorist bombing activity was escalating and that a previous SATO appointment was justified in preference to the previous system of emergency manning by SATOs from England.
>
> At the time of his appointment, the number of EOD incidents in the month was fifty-two, and this included two improvised explosive devices (IEDs) neutralised. Within ten months, the number of incidents had reached a peak of 672 including eighty devices neutralised.
>
> Major Styles, as SATO of the Command, was responsible for directing the activities of the ATO and AT EOD operators in Northern Ireland advising on neutralisation, operations, analysing EOD intelligence and disseminating it to his own operators and to CILSA for further analysis, and dissemination on British, NATO and ABCA EOD networks.
>
> On 20th October 1971, an RAOC team was called to deal with an explosive device in the new Europa Hotel in Belfast. It was clear that the bomb was

of a new and complicated type with an unusual number of anti-handling devices, and contained between ten and fifteen pounds of explosive. Major Styles personally took charge of the operation of neutralising, removing and dismantling the bomb, placing himself at risk to minimise the danger to the team. The whole operation took seven hours and was completely successful.

Two days later, the EOD team was again called to the Europa Hotel to deal with a second larger bomb, containing over thirty pounds of high explosive, even more anti-handling devices and a confusion of electrical circuits. It was clearly intended to defeat disarming techniques and kill the EOD operator attempting to neutralise it. Major Styles again assumed command of this operation and the bomb was disarmed, removed and dismantled. The second operation involved nine hours of intense and dangerous work.

In these two operations, the EOD operators led by Major Styles defeated two major attempts by the terrorists against the lives of innocent people and a prestige property target. The technical information obtained from the dismantling of the two bombs will undoubtedly help in avoiding loss of life in dealing with similar devices in the future.

The award of the George Cross to Major Styles brings not only great credit to the Corps, but it is also a tribute to all other RAOC EOD personnel who have been or may be employed on EOD duties in Northern Ireland, not forgetting the RAOC drivers, two of whom have been wounded in operations.

Warrant Officer Class 1 (SSM) Barry Johnson

WO1 (SSM) Barry Johnson of the Royal Army Ordnance Corps was awarded the George Cross for defuzing a series of mortar bombs left in a van near a hospital at Waterside, Londonderry.

The last bomb exploded as WO1 Johnson was dismantling it, causing serious injuries to his face and legs. He is now blind in one eye. His George Cross, the highest award for gallantry not on the battlefield, is the first for eleven years.

WO1 Johnson was in Northern Ireland on his second tour of duty and serving as a bomb disposal officer for 321 EOD Company RAOC when the call came on 7th October 1989. A vehicle containing an improvised IRA mortar device had been abandoned in the middle of a housing estate, close to a hospital.

He soon discovered that the mortar contained a live bomb in each of its six tubes and was intended for an attack on a Security Force base in the city. Aware of the grave danger to civilians, and in particular to patients in the hospital, he decided against the use of remote control equipment to deal with the bombs. Although this would have been normal practice – and would have placed him at much less personal risk, WO1 Johnson decided that there was too great a risk of launching one of the bombs during the remote-controlled render-safe procedure. He then set about removing the bombs from their tubes so that he could dismantle them by hand. He was fully aware that he might be operating against the clock and that the mortar could include an anti-handling device.

With the help of an assistant, he moved the firing tubes from the back of the vehicle to the ground, then sent his colleague behind cover so that he could carry out the extremely hazardous procedure alone. He also managed to place the tubes in such a way that if they fired, or the bombs detonated, the hospital would not be endangered. In the dark, in bitterly cold drizzle which made the handling of the heavy metal objects more precarious, he removed the bombs, dismantling each in turn.

Whilst he was working on the last one it blew. Completely blinded by the high velocity fragments, thrown across the road by the force of the explosion and in great pain, he would not allow his evacuation until he had briefed his assistant on the precise details of the device so that the operation could be safely completed by another EOD operator.

After months in hospital and many operations, Warrant Officer Johnson (38) is now back on duty. He is married, and he and his wife Maria have two children.

Born in London, he joined the Army Apprentices' College, Chepstow as an apprentice ammunition technician in 1967 at the age of 15, and completed his first tour as an EOD operator in Belfast in 1978. His second tour began last year, and during his service in the Province he completed 25 disposal tasks, including the neutralisation of nine live improvised explosive devices.

The George Cross was last awarded, posthumously, to Captain Robert Nairac, Grenadier Guards, in 1979 following his abduction and murder two years earlier by terrorists in Northern Ireland.

WO1 Johnson's award is only the second George Cross made to RAOC bomb disposal experts in Northern Ireland. The first was to Lieutenant Colonel George Styles in 1976. In all, members of the Corps have been awarded six George Crosses and sixty-five George Medals.

A selection of the citations for some of the other awards follows:

1940 – Acting Staff Sergeant John Hayton
British Empire Medal (Gallantry)

After air raids on Gibraltar, 24th and 25th September, the above party worked continuously searching and digging out unexploded enemy bombs, removing them by truck and dumping them at sea. [Cold blooded work, not in the heat of battle, which calls for steadiness and a high degree of courage.] They removed bombs varying from one hundred pounds to six hundred pounds, at the rate of one per day for ten days and, when reported on, were continuing the excellent and most dangerous work. All volunteered and have carried out work with great keenness and cheerfulness.

Originally recommended for the George Medal together with his working party of Acting Sergeant R. L. McIvide, Acting Lance Corporal L. Barratt, Acting Lance Corporal R. E. Sethcott, Privates G. V. Nicholson and B. Hatton.

In 1943 Lieutenant/Temporary Captain John Hayton BEM together with Lieutenant/Temporary Captain Francis East appears again.

Member of the Order of the British Empire (Gallantry)

On the 14th August 1943, unserviceable ammunition was being dumped at sea when a round exploded injuring two soldiers, one seriously.

The dumping was suspended and an investigation confirmed that there had been mishandling and that the explosion was caused by a misfired primer in a highly sensitive condition.

The explosion scattered 23 rounds which were each known to contain a misfired primer and likely to be in an even more sensitive condition. Before dumping could be resumed, these rounds had to be disposed of and Captain Hayton, assisted by Captain East, carried out this hazardous duty, personally searching for the scattered rounds, handling them and dumping them overboard. The handling of such rounds was a dangerous operation and in carrying it out successfully, both Captain Hayton and Captain East displayed a high sense of duty and cool courage.

1959 – Major W. C. Harrison
George Medal

The Queen has been graciously pleased to approve the award of the GEORGE MEDAL to Major William Clare HARRISON, MBE (232045), Royal Army Ordnance Corps, seconded to the Cyprus Police Force, in recognition of gallant and distinguished services.

Major Harrison was seconded to the Cyprus Police Force throughout the emergency as Government Explosives Expert. His duty was the examination and safe disposal of a wide variety of explosive devices, many of which were then set with time-pencils, or as 'Booby-Traps'. On occasions he personally entered buildings containing valuable equipment, and in which it was known that explosive time devices had been set, and at great personal risk rendered the devices safe and prevented further damage to property of considerable value and importance.

Whenever possible he personally attended to new devices to keep himself abreast of terrorist techniques, and to pass on the knowledge gained to his small staff. Major Harrison personally supervised the safe destruction of large quantities of explosives, much of them in a deteriorated and highly dangerous condition. His complete disregard for his own personal safety in the performance of his duty was of the highest order, and an example of courage and devotion to duty to all who have worked with him.

Staff Sergeant F. G. Giblett
George Medal

Staff Sergeant F. G. Giblett, RAOC has been awarded the GEORGE MEDAL for gallant and distinguished service in Cyprus. The citation reads:-

During a period of nearly three years, Staff Sergeant Giblett was employed on dangerous bomb disposal duties. Throughout this time he was on 24-hour call to the Larnaca Police, he dealt with a large number of explosive devices to be detonated by time fuzes and by fuzes responsive to movement or shock. He removed and disarmed a new pattern bomb fitted with complicated anti-handling devices, thereby preventing a major disaster in a petrol depot. On more than one occasion he was the first to enter hides, to make them safe from booby traps and to remove the extremely dangerous explosives and bombs which they contained.

Then, after a comrade had been killed on a new pattern mine, he bravely removed a similar device liable to explode on slight pressure.

In these and in other similar incidents, to prevent loss of life and damage to property, he repeatedly faced the grave danger of being killed. His conduct has been an example of great courage and constant devotion to duty.

1965 – Captain T. A. L. Judge
George Medal

The Queen approved the award of the GEORGE MEDAL to Captain T. A. L. Judge, RAOC.

The following is the citation published in the *London Gazette:* In the early hours of Wednesday, 15th July 1964, Captain Judge received an emergency call from the Assistant Commissioner of Police, Malacca, to examine a device including a brown paper carrier bag discovered beneath the Malacca Club and believed to be a bomb.

Captain Judge confirmed the package to be a timed demolition charge and requested the civil police to clear the densely populated area within a radius of 200 yards.

Captain Judge, who has disposed of a considerable number of such devices during the Malaysian emergency, being aware of the grave danger involved in the neutralisation of such complicated and sometimes unorthodox mechanisms, proceeded coolly and with great fortitude with the detailed examination.

This preliminary investigation revealed the timing device to be a modified wristlet watch, the normal face of which had been removed and the glass of which was covered partially by adhesive tape, thereby masking the possible time of detonation. Without regard for his personal safety, he bravely neutralised this fiendish mechanism within minutes of detonation and then fully disarmed the bomb. On subsequent examination of the timing device, his suspicions were confirmed that only a hair's breadth separated an alternative short circuit device of bared wires which, with the slightest movement, would also have detonated the explosive.

During the whole of this extremely delicate operation, Captain Judge never ceased to be aware of the danger with which he was confronted. In this instance and in many others prior to his departure from Malaysia, his cool courage and selfless devotion to the preservation and safety of human life in a young Commonwealth country were far beyond the call of normal duty. He never failed to respond swiftly to any demands, however dangerous the circumstances or however tired he might be.

1966 – Major C. W. Smith and Captain P. W. E. Istead
George Medal

The Queen has been graciously pleased to approve the award of the GEORGE MEDAL to the following RAOC officers – Major C. W. Smith and Captain P. W. E. Istead.

The following is the citation of the *London Gazette* in respect of Major C. W. Smith:

On the evening of Friday, 25th June 1965, a Belgian ammunition train caught fire in a cutting near Minden. The train had been stopped and four of the wagons uncoupled, but the fire increased and two of the wagons exploded, scattering shells over a wide area. Major C. W. Smith, who was at the time Senior Ammunition Officer, No. 3 Detachment No. 1 Ammunition Inspectorate, was telephoned as he was the ammunition advisor nearest to the scene. Although still some 80 miles away, he immediately went to the accident with his second in command, Captain P. W. E. Istead.

On arrival at the scene they found two of the wagons devastated and burning fiercely, whilst the adjoining wooden end of the third wagon was smouldering. The surrounding area was covered with burning propellant, exploded ammunition and a number of dangerously hot 90-millimetre shells, which might have exploded at any minute. The girders of the burning wagons were red hot in places, and there were still a number of unexploded rounds in the wreckage.

There was a large civilian house with a thatched roof within two hundred yards of the accident and despite the efforts of the German Police, a number of civilians were infiltrating into the area. A Royal Military Police non-commissioned officer, Lance Corporal Moodie, was trying to move a fire tender so that water could be played on the flames, but apart from this, nothing had been done to prevent further explosions and the local fire brigade were reluctant to approach.

Major Smith at once took charge of the situation. He first persuaded the fire brigade to move a tender to the top of the cutting overlooking the scene, and play water on the burning end of the third wagon. Then with complete disregard for his own safety, helped by Captain Istead, he broke into the third wagon and was just in time to move the ammunition boxes away from the risk of further explosion. Major Smith, assisted by Captain Istead and Lance Corporal Moodie, then uncoupled the third and fourth wagons, each containing about 10 tons of 90-millimetre ammunition and then moved them about 60 yards further down the track.

Having thus prevented a further major explosion, Major Smith set about dealing with the other ammunition which lay in and around the burning wagons. In most cases the projectiles were separated from the cases, but a number of complete rounds were still in smouldering cardboard cylinders. Some of the projectiles were marked 'Practice', but most of them had their markings burned off and were too hot to pick up with the naked hand. They all had to be treated as suspect and it was considered that in view of the likelihood of further explosions and the difficulty of discovering whether the shells were high explosive or not, the ammunition would have to be cooled with water before clearance could commence. In order not to expose the local firemen to undue hazard, Major Smith and Captain Istead handled the branch hose for the 30 minutes of this operation. Subsequently, with the aid of a fatigue party, all the ammunition was unloaded and removed.

The whole operation took twelve hours to complete, from about nine in the evening, when the officers arrived at the scene, until about nine-thirty the next morning, when all the ammunition had been cleared. Throughout this period, although he was well aware of the continuous danger of further explosions, Major Smith acted with utter disregard for his own safety, and in the highest tradition of the British Army.

The following is the citation for Captain P. W. E. Istead:

On the evening of Friday 25th June 1965, an ammunition train caught fire near Minden. The train had been stopped and four of the wagons uncoupled, but the fire increased and two of the wagons exploded scattering shells over a wide area. Captain P. W. E. Istead who was at the time Second in Command at No 3 Detachment, No 1 Ammunition Inspectorate, was instructed by his Commanding Officer to accompany the latter to the scene of the accident that was still some 80 miles away.

On arrival at the scene, they found two of the wagons devastated and burning fiercely, whilst the adjoining wagon was also burning. The surrounding area was covered with burning propellant, exploding ammunition and a number of dangerously hot 90-millimetre shells which might have exploded at any minute. The girders of the burning wagons were red hot in places and there were still a number of unexploded rounds in the wreckage. There was a large civilian house with a thatched roof within 200 yards of the accident and despite the efforts of the German Police a number of curious civilians were infiltrating the area. A Royal Military Police Non-Commissioned Officer, Lance Corporal Moodie, was trying to move a fire tender so that water could be played on the flames, but apart from this nothing had been done to prevent further explosions. The local fire brigade was reluctant to approach the burning wagons.

As soon as the fire brigade had moved the tender to the top of the cutting overlooking the scene and begun to play water on the burning end of the third wagon, Captain Istead accompanied his Officer Commanding on to the railway line. Then, with complete disregard for his own safety, he broke into the third wagon and was just in time to move the ammunition boxes away from the burning end before they too caught fire, and precipitated a further explosion. Immediately afterwards Captain Istead helped his Officer Commanding and the Non-Commissioned Officer to uncouple the third and fourth wagons, each containing about 10 tons of 90-millimetre ammunition, and move them about 60 yards down the track.

The problem now was how to deal with the other ammunition which lay in and around the burning wagons. In most cases the projectiles were separated from the cases but a number of complete rounds were still in smouldering cardboard cylinders in and around the wagon. Some of the projectiles around the wagon were marked 'Practice', but most of them had all their markings burnt off. They all had to be treated as suspect until examined. Most of the ammunition was too hot to pick up with the naked hand, and it was considered that in view of the likelihood of further explosions and the difficulty of discovering whether the shells were high explosive or not, the ammunition would have to be cooled with water before clearance could commence. In order not to expose the local firemen to undue hazard, Captain Istead handled the branch hose, together with

Major Smith, for the first 30 minutes of the operation. Subsequently, with the aid of a fatigue party, all the ammunition was unloaded and removed.

The whole operation took twelve hours to complete, from about nine in the evening, when the officers arrived at the scene, until about nine-thirty next morning, when all the ammunition had been cleared. Throughout this period, although he was well aware of the continuous danger of further explosions, Captain Istead acted with utter disregard for his own safety. Not only was the majority of the ammunition and two of the railway trucks saved, but the possibility of injury to civilians and damage to civilian property was also avoided. Captain Istead's fearless behaviour and the loyal and instant support which he gave to Major Smith was an inspiring example to those around him. His courageous actions in the face of continuous danger were in the highest traditions of the British Army.

Major H. J. Mitchell and Squadron Quartermaster Sergeant H. A. Vaughan
Member of the Order of the British Empire (Gallantry)

Major Mitchell and Warrant Officer Vaughan undertook a reconnaissance of Hell's Point and the Henderson Airfield Extension Area on Guadalcanal during the period 10th June to 6th July 1967, to assess the problems involved in the clearance of World War II ammunition in these areas. Hell's Point is the site of an American ammunition depot in which, during 1948 and again in 1953 there were a series of explosions lasting several days. On these occasions several members of the police were killed and a large quantity of ammunition was scattered about the area. The Henderson Airfield Extension Area was an American defensive position, on which there are still the remnants of gun sites and ammunition dumps.

The ammunition remaining in these two areas is scattered, often concealed by dense undergrowth and sometimes just below the surface. Ammunition of all types was found in varying stages of deterioration, including large quantities of fused high explosive shell, mortar bombs, grenades, Bangalore torpedoes, some filled with white phosphorous and some naval shells and aircraft bombs. Much of the ammunition was still in a highly dangerous state. Some fuses had also disintegrated leaving strikers poised over magazines without the protection of the safety devices. Other fuses were exuding dangerous and extremely sensitive explosive compositions.

Additionally, some shells and bombs were unstable, having been involved in previous detonations. Some grenade strikers were held back only by rust, while certain shells filled with white phosphorus, burst into flames on moving. Detonations are commonplace, and are an accepted part of the life of the inhabitants. Major Mitchell and Warrant Officer Vaughan were thus well aware of the likelihood of further explosions and these did not occur during their work. Major Mitchell took charge of the situation, and with Warrant Officer Vaughan proceeded coolly and with great fortitude to do a detailed reconnaissance of Hell's Point, estimating that approximately 5,000 tons of ammunition still remained there to be cleared.

At Henderson Airfield Major Mitchell, in order to avoid the possibility of injury to civilians and damage to property, decided to extend the team's stay, and clear this area of ammunition. This was achieved in three weeks but only by working very long hours under extremely adverse and exacting conditions.

In all, 12,000 shells, bombs, grenades and mines were removed from this area and dumped in the sea by Major Mitchell and Warrant Officer Vaughan. However, 47 projectiles, including 'blinds', were destroyed in situ, because they were too dangerous to move.

Much of the ammunition had to be removed by hand, holding it centrally in a horizontal position in order to prevent any contact of fuse strikers with the sensitive explosives and to minimise the effects of any sudden movement. This was hazardous work carried out without regard to their own safety. Local inhabitants provided to assist were only allowed to handle ammunition that was entirely safe. Throughout the operation Major Mitchell, remote from any superior authority or source of advice and never knowing the extent of danger embodied in any one projectile, took difficult decisions and assumed heavy responsibilities, thereby demonstrating exceptional initiative, resourcefulness and prowess. He was supported throughout and without hesitation by Warrant Officer Vaughan.

Conductor S. G. Woods
Member of the Order of the British Empire (Gallantry)

From late July to 16th October 1967, Warrant Officer Class 1 Woods, Royal Army Ordnance Corps, was engaged in disposing of bombs which were planted in large numbers by Communist terrorists throughout Hong Kong and particularly in the densely populated urban area.

In the first two months of this period he carried out more than twenty tours of this very arduous duty, none of less than 12 hours, during which he dealt with nearly 300 devices. Not all were true bombs, but hoax bombs, deliberately designed to give the appearance of true ones, had to be handled with equal care; and in this initial phase of the campaign, all had to be dismantled and their potential assessed, in order that the most effective means of disposal could be devised.

As reinforcement technicians arrived, Warrant Officer Woods took them out into the streets, carefully instructing them in the methods and procedures to be used.

The work on which he was engaged was made even more dangerous by the terrorist tactic of using a device, true or hoax, to attract a target in the form of a bomb disposal team and then throwing down further bombs from nearby buildings.

A number of persons, military, police and civilians were killed during this campaign, and a large number were injured. Despite this Warrant Officer Woods repeatedly exposed himself to danger, until he himself was injured dealing with a device on 16th October. His gallant and devoted conduct, which was in the highest traditions of the service, was an inspiration to his colleagues and gained the admiration of all who were associated with him in this highly dangerous and demanding work.

Sergeant D. L. Birch
British Empire Medal (Gallantry)

From 28th July to 9th October 1967, Sergeant Birch, Royal Army Ordnance Corps, was engaged in disposing of bombs during the terrorist campaign of bomb planting in Hong Kong. In this time he carried out no less than twenty periods of duty and dealt with more than 200 devices. Although not all devices proved to be true bombs all had to be most carefully and exhaustively investigated and dealt with.

This dangerous work was made even more so by the terrorist stratagem of using a device, true or hoax, to attract the target in the form of the bomb disposal team, and then throwing further bombs down from nearby buildings. A number of personnel were killed or injured in this campaign of terrorism; Sergeant Birch was himself injured by a bomb thrown during his investigation of a device. Despite these dangers, and his injury, Sergeant Birch continued coolly and fearlessly with his demanding task.

His calm courage was an example of gallantry of a high order which was an inspiration to his colleagues and in the highest tradition of the service.

Acting Captain Roger Frederick Mendham
George Medal

This officer was commissioned into the RAOC from RMA Sandhurst in July 1967 and within four years was promoted to his present acting rank in February 1971 on completion of an Ammunition Technical Officers (ATO) Course. The course, apart from dealing with normal conventional ammunition matters, also qualified him for duties in Explosive Ordnance Disposal (EOD). He was attached to 321 EOD unit RAOC during the period 1st October 1971 – 2nd February 1972 and served throughout in Belfast.

Captain Mendham arrived in Ulster within a few days of the death of Captain D. Stewardson, RAOC, who was killed whilst dismantling a device which was subsequently to become known by EOD personnel as a 'Castle Robin'. Both officers had attended the same ATO course and were close friends.

The period was one of intense activity, and Captain Mendham was involved in many incidents that caught the public eye by both TV and Press reports. He was involved with both bombs planted by terrorists in the Europa Hotel on the 20th and 22nd October 1971. The story of these events has achieved international recognition. A few days afterwards on 4th November 1971 he was instrumental in dismantling a clockwork mechanism found in the York Hotel. The task lasted nine hours and involved Captain Mendham in considerable personal danger as he attempted to lift the device clear on a long pole.

On 25th November 1971 Captain Mendham personally dismantled no less than four devices and answered calls to six further incidents.

There were several occasions when he missed death by seconds. The first of these happened early in his tour. On 24th October, having completed his initial reconnaissance of a device in the Celebrity Club, he was just leaving the building when the bomb exploded. A similar incident occurred in Duncairn Gardens, on 29th October 1971, when the device exploded and brought the house down around him. A further occasion was on 13th November 1971, when a bomb exploded just as he was leaving after his initial reconnaissance. On this same day Captain Mendham attended a further six incidents without displaying any qualms or fear despite so narrow an escape from death.

During his tour in Belfast Captain Mendham personally answered 235 calls, whilst the small team under his command dealt with no less than 936 requests for their services in the period.

Such activity inevitably imposed great strain upon all concerned and it is to Captain Mendham's lasting credit, and due to his constant display of courage, leadership and technical proficiency, that nobody succumbed to the tension but rather grew in stature because of it.

For one so young, this concentration of experience and ready acceptance of responsibility brought forth a response of the highest order well worthy of formal recognition.

Warrant Officer Class 1 Peter Edwin Spencer Gurney
George Medal

Warrant Officer Class 1 Gurney became an Ammunition Technician in 1950. He served a four months tour of bomb disposal duty from 9th August 1972 to 9th December 1972 as Senior Ammunition Technician of No 1 Section, 321 Explosive Ordnance Disposal Unit, Royal Army Ordnance Corps. He was part of a team of six operators in support of 39 Infantry Brigade, the team being based in the City of Belfast. During his tour he dealt with 123 bomb incidents and personally made safe or detonated safely 25 live bombs.

Warrant Officer Gurney is one of the Corps' most experienced Ammunition Technicians. He was sent into Northern Ireland to assist the young Ammunition Technical Officer who led the section. Some of his major neutralisations are cited in this recommendation.

On 22nd August 1972 he was tasked to a 50lb bomb placed by armed men in a public house in Belfast. As the men left they told the occupants that the bomb had an anti-handling device. One bar customer picked up the bomb and threw it outside. Warrant Officer Gurney placed his classified neutralisation equipment by hand and completely and safely disrupted it.

On 22nd September 1972 he dealt with a 40lb bomb in an unused Social Club in Belfast. Once more he used the classified equipment placing it by hand and completely disrupted the bomb which had been booby trapped to appear as two bags of explosives. His actions took only ten minutes. His training and experience told him to treat the bags as a complete bomb. A less experienced operator would probably have picked up the bags and been killed.

He continued to make excellent use of the classified equipment but was in the forefront of the use and experimentation of the potential of remote handling equipment for bomb disposal work.

On 27th November 1972 he was tasked to a derelict house in the Ardoyne area of Belfast. A patrol had been called to look inside through a hole in the door and had called for a bomb disposal expert once they had noticed a taut piece of string inside. Warrant Officer Gurney immediately suspected a booby trap device. He forced an entry through a house nearby and saw eventually that the taut string was linked to an insulating wedge in the jaws of a clothes peg switch to a five pound bomb. The entire action was completed in five minutes and the bomb was made safe.

Later the same day he dealt with another booby trap of 75lbs. A patrol had reported a find in a pipe; explosives could be seen. Once again Warrant

Officer Gurney carried out his actions as if the explosive were a bomb. He hooked out five pounds of explosives then noticed a wire. He caused the pipe to be moved away from its location, the front wall of a boilerhouse, and tipped it up to empty its contents. The contents of the pipe were booby trapped so that further pulling action would bring two bare wires into contact thus exploding the bomb. He calmly directed the action, dealt with the bomb by hand and made it safe.

These were typical of his professional approach, his cool work, his complete disregard for danger because of his mastery of his trade. His actions were in the highest traditions of the British Army.

Staff Sergeant Alan Victor Glasby
George Medal

Staff Sergeant Glasby served with Headquarters 321 EOD Unit RAOC from 9th October 1972 to 25th October 1973. His primary task was to record intelligence and prepare statistics on terrorist bombs. His secondary duty was as an ATO with the HQ Section 321 EOD Unit RAOC dealing with the RUC Division R and reinforcing other sections when necessary.

His primary duties were performed with intelligence and skill. It was as an ATO that his exceptional practical ability, calmness in difficult and dangerous situations and cheerful willingness to undertake long arduous periods of duty earned him the admiration and respect of his fellow ATOs and all security forces with whom he worked.

On 17th May 1973 a telephone warning was received of a bomb in the ladies' toilet at Lisburn Railway Station. It was placed by a young woman who persuaded an attendant to let her into the closed toilet. The narrow access and swing doors made it impossible to use a Wheelbarrow to approach the bomb remotely.

Staff Sergeant Glasby ensured that all Security Forces and public were at a safe distance before entering the toilet. The 50lb bomb initiated by a cooker timer was wedged behind the bowl.

Staff Sergeant Glasby successfully disrupted the bomb, cut out the detonator and recovered the circuit which yielded fingerprints. The timer had made contact and when subsequently tried the circuit worked every time. As a result of the evidence recovered two members of the PIRA including the female planter were arrested and are soon to appear for trial. Detonation of the bomb would have destroyed the railway station and probably caused a lengthy blockage on the main Belfast line.

On 2nd July 1973 a barge used for collecting sand from Loch Neagh was found to smell strongly of marzipan when boarded by her master at 0815. Staff Sergeant Glasby boarded the barge and traced the device to a greasy catwalk in the ill lit engine room ten feet below decks and approachable only through a narrow hatchway and down a narrow flight of vertical steps. The 50lb bomb would have demolished the barge had it gone off.

Staff Sergeant Glasby climbed down the ladder into the engine room, placed his disruptive equipment and successfully separated the initiating circuit from the explosive. He re-entered the barge and cut out the detonator and recovered the explosive. Poor electrical contact was responsible for the failure of the bomb but the contacts were in perfect working order when subsequently tested. This was a particularly hazardous EOD operation where a slip during the placing of the disrupter could have set off the bomb.

At Deer Park near Gally Gate Loch Neagh on 5 October 1973 he was dismantling an 85lb device placed in a milk churn at the side of the road. During this process he attached a tow rope to the churn and dragged it with a Saracen causing it to cross the road and fall into thick undergrowth on the other side. On going forward he found a second churn well concealed in the undergrowth with the clock still going. He calmly attached a line and pulled clear the initiating circuit thus defeating a terrorist attempt to kill Security Forces responding to the detonation of the first bomb, by causing a second to detonate later in the same location.

Throughout his year of duty Staff Sergeant Glasby never failed to volunteer for additional duty when sections were heavily committed. He successfully neutralised 8 of the 19 genuine bombs in the 57 incidents to which he was tasked and gave valuable assistance in the briefing and training of newly trained ATOs.

Lieutenant Colonel John Maurice Gaff
George Medal

Lieutenant Colonel Gaff has been the Chief Ammunition Technical Officer, Northern Ireland from 13th February to 1st November 1974. During this period he has not only displayed outstanding qualities of leadership but has also, on innumerable occasions, exhibited great personal courage by himself neutralising terrorist bombs in conditions of great danger.

One incident, which deserves particular mention, took place on 21st March 1974. Lieutenant Colonel Gaff was summoned to the Railway Signal House at Dunloy Halt where three armed men had placed a bomb in the building and a second bomb on the railway track. Lieutenant Colonel Gaff assumed command of the operation and himself quickly defused the bomb on the railway track. However, the bomb in the Railway House proved to be more difficult to neutralise as its exact position was not known and it was suspected that it was booby trapped because the terrorists had spent such a considerable amount of time in the building. For nearly eight hours Lieutenant Colonel Gaff investigated every inch of the Signal Box despite the extreme danger involved in this activity. Finally he noticed a small bump at the bottom of the stairwell under a piece of linoleum and this turned out to be the pressure switch of the booby trap. It was clearly a sensitive device and Lieutenant Colonel Gaff had to place the disruptive equipment alongside the pressure switch, knowing that the slightest pressure in the wrong place would trigger the device resulting in him being killed or badly injured. His action proved successful and the booby trap circuit was disrupted. He then searched for the main explosive charge which he eventually found under the stairs. It consisted of seventy pounds of explosives. This whole operation took nearly fifteen hours during which time Lieutenant Colonel Gaff was in extreme personal danger. This successful neutralisation avoided any damage being caused to the Signal Box and its equipment and enabled an important railway line to be kept open.

Throughout the long potentially dangerous time that Lieutenant Colonel Gaff was neutralising the bomb he displayed outstanding personal courage and technical skill which were an example to the men of his unit and also to the general public as a whole, as his operation attracted attention of the media. By his calm professional behaviour he averted what could have been a most successful terrorist attack which could have caused death or injury to members of the public or to members of the Security Forces who were operating in this area. This particular action typifies the outstanding personal courage and devotion to duty which Lieutenant Colonel Gaff demonstrated throughout his tour of Northern Ireland in an extremely hazardous and highly technical field of operations.

Warrant Officer Class 2 K. F. A. Adams
George Medal

Warrant Officer Class 2 Adams served with No 3 Section EOD Unit as the Ammunition Technical Officer located at Omagh from 1st February 1977 to 9th June 1977. He was sent to Northern Ireland to replace an ATO who had been killed whilst attempting to neutralise a device in January. This was his second tour as an ATO in Northern Ireland. He served previously for 4 months from November 1971 to March 1972.

The area in which WO2 Adams worked, Tyrone and Fermanagh, is notorious for the number of booby trap devices designed specifically to kill the ATO. During his four month tour the region was particularly active. He was tasked 65 times during his 4 months of which 25 were actual devices. He neutralised 13 devices, of which 4 were booby trapped.

On 19th February he was tasked to a Garand clip of 8 rounds lying in the grass near the Drumcard road about 1km from Kinawley. On the 16th February an RUC (R) Constable had been shot and wounded. During the follow up search of the firing point area a full clip of Garand rounds was found with an unidentifiable object underneath. In an operation lasting 2 days he successfully neutralised a device consisting of 4½lbs of Frangex explosive with a timing unit and micro switch. His meticulous care enabled the explosive to be traced to the mine in the Republic from which it had been stolen.

On 23rd February he was tasked to a device jammed between the outside mesh and frame of a window of the Community Centre in Omagh. A previous telephone call had warned of a booby trap in the area. In an operation lasting 5 hours he successfully neutralised a device consisting of ½lb of explosive in a metal pipe.

On 23rd April he was tasked to an explosion near to the M23 Border Crossing. The explosion was a deliberate 'come on' to lure the Security Forces into the area. In an operation lasting over 6 hours he successfully neutralised 2 booby trapped devices each consisting of more than 50lbs of home made explosive. He had to make a series of manual approaches to each device in order to render each bomb safe.

On 7th May he was tasked to a device under the cat walk on top of a 12,000 gallon fuel tank in McMullan's Fuel Depot, Omagh. The device, which consisted of 11lbs of home made explosive, was difficult to reach. If it had functioned at any time during the clearance operation the result would have been catastrophic and would have killed the ATO. He successfully neutralised the device in an operation lasting almost 3 hours.

These incidents reflect the high technical skill and personal courage required for a successful clearance operation. WO2 Adams was always in complete control of the situation and by his example, confidence, and professional skill earned the respect of all those with whom he served. His actions are all the more outstanding because he was fully aware that his predecessor had been killed whilst carrying out the same tasks.

His fine example, professional skill and personal courage were in keeping with the high standards of his fellow bomb disposal operators.

Perhaps the following brief summary for a very gallant soldier is the most telling.

Special Promotion of 7515 Private L. J. Cheetham for Gallantry in the Field

D.D.O.S. 2nd Army
7515 Pte L J Cheetham A. O. Corps.
In forwarding the attached recommendation for advancement in promotion and Corps pay of the man above mentioned, I beg to point out that in addition to ordinary departmental qualifications he has twice recently shown that he possesses courage and ability above average.

(Signed) H. B. Johnson, Lieut.
O. O., 5th Corps Troops.
12.5.15

From Major General Sir J Steevens, K.C.B., K.C.M.G., D.E.O.S.
To the Director of Ordnance Services,
British Expeditionary Force.
War Office, Whitehall S.W. 26 May 1915

The report concerning an act of daring and resource on the part of No. 7515 Pte L. J. Cheetham, Army Ordnance Corps, which you forwarded under cover of your O.S.R./1188, is evidence of the splendid spirit which many officers, and others who have been in France, have told me is very marked in the Warrant Officers, Non Commissioned Officers and men in the Corps.

There have been greater opportunities in this campaign than in any previous ones for the Corps to emerge from behind the scenes and if they all grasped them in the manner described in your report, the Corps may be well proud of itself.

Private Cheetham may be promoted to Full Corporal from the date of the occurrence, and this will be confirmed in due course by the Officer Commanding, Army Ordnance Corps.

(Signed) J. Steevens
Director of Equipment and Ordnance Stores

Army Ordnance Corps (old force)
Corps Orders by Colonel C. Tufnell, Officer i/c Records,
Red Barracks, Woolwich
1st June 1915

NO. 294 SPECIAL PROMOTION FOR ACTS OF DARING AND RESOURCE IN THE FIELD
7515 Pte Cheetham, L. J., Expeditionary Force. To be CORPORAL 11.5.15
On the night of 11th May 1915, Pte Cheetham accompanied a party to a camp in Ypres to collect 160,000 rounds of 0.303" ammunition. The convoy was shelled during the operation of loading and when the non commissioned officer in charge was no longer in a position to direct operations, Pte Cheetham took charge, succeeding in steadying the rest of the party and, in doing so, enabled the whole of the ammunition to be loaded and brought the convoy back in safety to headquarters.

On a previous occasion at Poperinghe, after the office had been wrecked by a 12" enemy shell, he acted with great coolness.

List of Awards to Members of the Corps with Names and Dates

At the School of Ammunition there is now a record of all awards for Gallantry held by Ammunition Technicians or Technical Officers from the 1960s and, in some cases, dating back to 1940. However, there is no definitive list of those specific awards to the trade for the First World War. In those days, there was no similar trade, in fact some officers were not even members of the Corps. In an attempt to record all the gallantry awards for ammunition-related incidents I have prepared the following lists presented in the appendix. I realise that it will not be complete but thought it better to try to produce a record than miss them all off for fear of criticism from readers. I apologise sincerely in advance for any omissions.

A Summary of the Awards:

OBE	23	1973–1994
DCM	5	1917–1918
MC	26	1916–1919
MM	8	1917–1918
MSM	8	1917–1927
GC	6	1949–1990
GM	66	1940–1995
MBE	45	1942–1994
BEM	26	1940–1974
QGM	73	1974–1994

APPENDIX

ROLL OF HONOUR

ORDER OF THE BRITISH EMPIRE (OBE)

Capt E M Ketley	1943	England
Lieut Col P L Crosby	1973	Northern Ireland
Lieut Col M H McKenzie-Orr	1974	Northern Ireland
Lieut Col P M Underhill	1976	Northern Ireland
Lieut Col D Patrick	1977	Northern Ireland
Lieut Col P W E Istead GM	1978	Northern Ireland
Lieut Col B R Fox	1979	Northern Ireland
Lieut Col B Forshaw	1980	Northern Ireland
Lieut Col G M G Hendry	1981	Northern Ireland
Lieut Col L Guy	1982	Northern Ireland
Lieut Col T C K Ridley	1984	Northern Ireland
Lieut Col M D Hall	1985	Northern Ireland
Lieut Col W J Manuel	1986	Northern Ireland
Lieut Col J R Hawkins	1987	Northern Ireland
Lieut Col Courtney-Green	1987	England
Lieut Col H G Heap	1988	Northern Ireland
Lieut Col R N Lennox	1989	Northern Ireland
Lieut Col Baughan	1989	Germany
Lieut Col D N Furness-Gibbon	1989	Northern Ireland
Lieut Col A V Glasby	1991	Northern Ireland
Lieut Col P C Maynard	1992	Northern Ireland
Lieut Col R A Swindley	1994	Northern Ireland
Lieut Col C R Elderton	1994	Northern Ireland

DISTINGUISHED CONDUCT MEDAL (DCM)

Pte H W Wood	1917	France
A Sub Condr T A Harding	1917	France
T Sub Condr H S J Beckett	1918	France
T Sub Condr G L Harris	1918	France
A Sub Condr P H Richley	1917	France

MILITARY CROSS (MC)

Lieut J P Read	1916	France
Capt A J Gatt (Malta RA)	1916	France
Lieut F A J Lock	1916	France
Capt T Donovan RGA	1917	France
Lieut R M Fisher	1917	France
Capt D Leslie	1917	France
Capt H J Gee Bartome	1917	France
T/Lieut F W Lewis	1917	France
Capt C F T Haigh	1917	France
A/Capt B G G Harris	1917	France

MILITARY CROSS (MC) continued

Lieut R F Craighead	1918	France
Lieut E P Corbert Sulivan	1918	France
Lieut A J Johnson RGA – Bar to MC	1918	France
A/Capt H G Alaway	1918	France
A/Capt J U M Bailey	1918	France
T/Capt C Banfield RGA	1918	France
A/Capt R G Body RFA	1918	France
A/Capt C R Douglas	1918	France
T/Lieut J R Douglas	1918	France
A/Capt A G Hackett	1918	France
Lieut Comley Hawkes	1918	France
T/Lieut W H L Somerville	1918	France
T/Lieut T B Vinycomb	1918	France
Hon Lieut/Ass Com of Ord A B W Fletcher	1918	France
Lieut H Morrison	1919	France
Lieut H J Steer	1919	France

MILITARY MEDAL (MM)

S/Condr A E Harris	1917	France
Cpl H Jones	1917	France
Pte W Branda	1917	France
Sgt E T Pope	1917	France
S/Condr A C Bancroft	1918	France
S/Sgt A W Jasper	1918	France
Pte A J W Baxter	1918	France
Pte F J Cross	1918	France

MERITORIOUS SERVICE MEDAL (MSM) 1916-1928

Cpl H A Owen	1917	Egypt
S/Condr S Shepherd	1917	France
Sgt G T Crew	1918	France
S/Condr W J Lloyd	1919	France
Sgt W Gallagher	1921	Iraq
L/Sgt W J Jewell	1921	Iraq
S/Sgt M B Matheson	1927	India (Indian AOC)
S/Condr G E Turner	1927	India (Indian AOC)

GEORGE CROSS (GC)

Capt R L Jephson Jones	1940	Malta
Lieut W M Eastman	1940	Malta
T/Maj K A Biggs	1946	Savernake
A/SSgt S G Rogerson	1946	Savernake
Maj S G Styles	1972	Northern Ireland
WO1 (SSM) B Johnson	1990	Northern Ireland

NB: Major K A Biggs was also awarded the US Bronze Star for the 1946 Savernake incident.

GEORGE MEDAL (GM)

T/Capt D A S Martin	1940	Gibraltar
T/Capt R Cjalkley	1940	
A/Capt F V Plater	1941	Toura
A/Sgt L Telford	1941	Toura
SSgt E P Thorner	1941	Toura
T/Capt T W Downing	1943	Northern Ireland
T/Maj R W H Beaton	1944	Italy
T/Maj W Whittles	1944	Italy
Sgt F W Pearce	1944	England
Sgt J S McGowan	1944	France
Maj G C Pepper	1944	France
T/Capt M F Smith	1946	Emden
Sgt D A Kay	1946	Savernake
A/WO1 E R Robson	1947	Zayatkwin
A/Sgt K W Nash	1948	Saxelby
Capt R V Harley	1951	England
Sgt A T Taylor	1957	Cyprus
Capt G Prosser	1957	Northern Ireland
A/Sgt J T Proudlock	1957	Cyprus
SSgt F G Giblett	1959	Cyprus
Maj W C Harrison MBE	1959	Cyprus
Maj W Musson	1964	Aldershot
WO1 S Brazier	1964	Aldershot
Maj P S Easterby MBE	1965	Cyprus
Capt T A L Judge	1965	Malaya
Maj C W Smith	1966	Minden
Capt P W E Istead	1966	Minden
Capt M D Hall	1966	Malaya
WO2 B J Reid	1966	Malaya
Maj J F Elliott	1966	Aden
Maj G C Brownlee	1968	Aden
Capt A I Clouter	1972	Northern Ireland
WO2 T J Green	1972	Northern Ireland
Capt D Markham	1972	Northern Ireland
Capt R F Mendham	1972	Northern Ireland
Sgt A E Dedman	1972	Northern Ireland
WO2 P H Dandy	1973	Northern Ireland
WO2 B J Mitchell	1973	Northern Ireland
WO2 J M Coldrick MBE	1973	Northern Ireland
Capt H D McCormack	1973	Northern Ireland
Capt M F Stacy	1973	Northern Ireland
WO2 C B Tennant	1973	Northern Ireland
WO1 P E S Gurney	1973	Northern Ireland
Sgt K Callaghan	1973	Northern Ireland
WO1 F H Eldred	1973	Northern Ireland
Capt J N Gunson	1973	Northern Ireland
Maj M W Newcombe	1973	Northern Ireland
Capt C Field	1973	Northern Ireland
Lieut Col M H McKenzie-Orr MBE	1974	Northern Ireland
SSgt A V Glasby	1974	Northern Ireland
SSgt A G Griffin	1974	Northern Ireland
Maj J Q Jackson MBE	1974	Northern Ireland

GEORGE MEDAL (GM) continued

WO2 D Oldham	1974	Northern Ireland
Lt Col J M Gaff	1975	Northern Ireland
SSgt R V Bruce	1977	Northern Ireland
WO2 K F A Adams	1977	Northern Ireland
SSgt G Goodrum	1978	Northern Ireland
Sgt J A Anderson	1980	Northern Ireland
Maj M J Davison	1986	Northern Ireland
WO2 P M Hurry	1988	Northern Ireland
WO2 M G Knox	1989	Northern Ireland
Capt K Mollison	1991	Northern Ireland
Maj M Blatherwick	1991	Northern Ireland
WO2 D A Duffy BEM	1992	Northern Ireland
WO1 J T Balding	1993	Northern Ireland
WO1 N B Thomsen	1995	Northern Ireland

MEMBER OF THE ORDER OF THE BRITISH EMPIRE (MBE FOR GALLANTRY) (AWARD CHANGED IN 1974 TO QUEEN'S GALLANTRY MEDAL)

T/Capt K R Baker	1942	England
T/Capt F R East	1943	England
T/Capt J Hayton BEM	1943	England
WOl F W Goldiman	1946	Savernake
Maj M A Emery	1967	Wareham
Maj H J Mitchell	1968	Guadalcanal
WO2 H A Vaughan	1968	Guadalcanal
WOl S G Woods	1968	Hong Kong
Maj C M Jefferies	1968	Wales
WOl F W Wood	1968	Wales
Capt M F Steward	1971	Northern Ireland
Capt M J Davison	1974	Northern Ireland
Capt P C Maynard	1974	Northern Ireland
WOl F Hodge	1974	Northern Ireland

MEMBER OF THE ORDER OF THE BRITISH EMPIRE (MBE)

Capt R Buffham	1976	Scotland
Capt R P Jennings	1978	Northern Ireland
Maj G J Browne	1978	Northern Ireland
Maj J B Owen	1979	Northern Ireland
Maj C J Ahearne	1979	Northern Ireland
Maj D R Hodgens	1980	Northern Ireland
WO1 M Heath	1980	Northern Ireland
Maj D N Furness Gibbon	1981	Northern Ireland
WO2 P Mitchell QGM	1982	Northern Ireland
Maj J N Gunson GM	1983	Northern Ireland
Maj A F Gibson	1985	Northern Ireland
Capt J Carr	1985	Northern Ireland
Maj R A Swindley	1985	Northern Ireland
Maj M K Watkins	1986	Northern Ireland
Capt R A Abson	1987	Northern Ireland
WO1 G C Chudley	1988	Northern Ireland
Maj M Blatherwick	1989	Northern Ireland

MEMBER OF THE ORDER OF THE BRITISH EMPIRE (MBE)
continued

Maj A P Williams	1989	Northern Ireland
WO1 N J Nice	1989	England
WOl R G Whitford	1990	England
WO1 D J Leadbetter	1991	Gulf
Capt J L A Earey QGM	1992	Northern Ireland
WO1 WDG Hunt	1993	Northern Ireland
Maj J A Jones	1993	Northern Ireland
WO2 P M Williams	1993	Northern Ireland
Maj M I Dolamore	1994	England
WO1 D Cotterill	1994	Northern Ireland
Maj A D Farron	1994	Northern Ireland
Maj G A O'Sullivan	1994	Northern Ireland
Capt P M Swift	1994	Northern Ireland
WO1 R W Travers	1994	Northern Ireland

Two civilian members of the Reasearch and Development Department at Fort Halstead must also be recorded:

Mike Barker	1971	Pigstick
Lofty Pattinson	1972	Wheelbarrow

For development work on the equipment in England and in Northern Ireland

BRITISH EMPIRE MEDAL (BEM FOR GALLANTRY)

A/SSgt J Hayton	1940	Gibraltar
Cpl A J Adams	1946	Savernake
SSgt P Anderson	1954	Hong Kong
WO1 C P McKernan	1954	Northern Ireland
SSgt D W Pittaway	1954	Northern Ireland
A/WO2 E R Worswick	1956	Malaya
Sgt R F Goad	1958	Cyprus
Sgt R W McDonald	1958	Cyprus
SSgt D H Stephenson	1960	Malaya
Sgt D L Birch	1968	Hong Kong
Sgt I C J M Carrier	1971	Northern Ireland
Sgt R L Lockwood	1971	Northern Ireland
A/WO2 T C Park	1971	Northern Ireland
Sgt R B Crisp	1972	Northern Ireland
Sgt G Neath	1973	Northern Ireland
SSgt M A Anfield	1973	Northern Ireland
SSgt G M Wright	1973	Northern Ireland
SSgt A Steward	1973	Northern Ireland
WO2 T N Galloway	1973	Northern Ireland
SSgt R R P Kirby	1974	Northern Ireland
A/WO2 G A Wells	1974	Northern Ireland
Sgt J G Lightfoot	1974	Northern Ireland
SSgt D Greenaway	1974	Northern Ireland
Sgt F Haley	1974	Northern Ireland
SSgt I J F Munro	1974	Northern Ireland
Sgt J V Fazackerly	1974	Northern Ireland

QUEEN'S GALLANTRY MEDAL (QGM)

SSgt A R Carter	1974	Northern Ireland
Cpl J P Fletcher	1974	Northern Ireland
WO1 R Gill	1974	Northern Ireland
Capt P V Snell	1974	Northern Ireland
WO1 G E Barrow	1975	Northern Ireland
SSgt A A Burns	1975	Northern Ireland
Capt R J Dace	1975	Northern Ireland
Capt J F D Serle	1975	Northern Ireland
SSgt H Blinkhorn	1975	Northern Ireland
WO1 T E Robinson	1975	Northern Ireland
Capt N N Wylde	1975	Northern Ireland
Maj C R Pickard	1975	Northern Ireland
WO2 F J Murphy	1975	Northern Ireland
SSgt C J Kilduff	1976	Northern Ireland
SSgt P Mitchell	1976	Northern Ireland
SSgt P J Sanders	1976	Northern Ireland
Sgt D M Couling	1977	Northern Ireland
Sgt D J Silvester	1977	Northern Ireland
WO2 C B Lambert	1977	Northern Ireland
WO1 C P McKernan	1977	Northern Ireland
Sgt C D Kerr	1977	Northern Ireland
WO1 R D Boucher	1977	Northern Ireland
WO2 A J Burgess	1978	Northern Ireland
SSgt C T Creighton	1978	Northern Ireland
SSgt A Shoemaker	1979	Northern Ireland
SSgt G Ferguson	1979	Northern Ireland
WO2 I T Grey	1980	Northern Ireland
WO2 K Callaghan	1980	Northern Ireland
Capt M C Wickham	1980	Northern Ireland
WO2 M C Boscott	1980	Northern Ireland
SSgt S J Wilks	1981	Northern Ireland
WO2 J O Unsworth	1982	Northern Ireland
Capt M Kerley	1982	Northern Ireland
WO1 D Walker	1982	Northern Ireland
SSgt M Berridge	1983	Northern Ireland
Capt G A O'Sullivan	1984	Northern Ireland
Maj A J Taylor	1984	Northern Ireland
Maj R P Jennings MBE	1984	Northern Ireland
Capt P Harris	1984	Northern Ireland
WO1 F W Srnith	1985	Northern Ireland
Capt I P Nunn	1985	Northern Ireland
WO1 G Ferguson (Bar see 1979)	1985	Northern Ireland
Capt M M Grieveson	1986	Northern Ireland
WO2 J L A Earey	1986	Northern Ireland
WO1 E L Bienkowski	1987	Northern Ireland
SSgt R J Scott	1987	Northern Ireland
SSgt R A L Trude	1987	Northern Ireland
WO2 B Taylor	1987	Greece
Capt S P Dowe	1988	Northern Ireland
WO2 M G Finan	1988	Northern Ireland
SSgt S Hooper	1988	Northern Ireland
WO2 M Hawkins	1988	Northern Ireland

QUEEN'S GALLANTRY MEDAL (QGM) continued

Sgt G J Lamont	1988	Northern Ireland
SSgt S P Holmes	1988	Northern Ireland
Capt C H Hodder	1988	Northern Ireland
WO2 S O'Brien	1989	Northern Ireland
SSgt J F Clarke	1989	Northern Ireland
Sgt I Mapp	1989	Northern Ireland
SSgt N P Menzies	1989	Northern Ireland
SSgt J H Franks	1989	Northern Ireland
WO2 J P Grimsly	1989	Northern Ireland
Capt R L Maybery	1990	Northern Ireland
WO2 S A Turner	1991	Northern Ireland
SSgt A Islam	1991	Northern Ireland
Capt R C Davies	1992	Northern Ireland
Capt A N E Salmons	1992	Northern Ireland
WO2 N McDonald	1993	Northern Ireland
Maj A R Wallace	1994	Northern Ireland
Capt P G Smith	1994	England
WO2 R A Wharton	1994	England
SSgt A N Joy	1994	Northern Ireland
WO1 R J McLelland	1994	Northern Ireland
Capt C J Henson	1995	Northern Ireland

HOME OFFICE AND METROPOLITAN POLICE

GEORGE CROSS

Goad, Roger Philips BEM	Terrorist Device, London	October 1976

Capt Goad, an explosives officer employed by the Metropolitan Police, was on 29 August 1975 called to examine a suspect package in a shop doorway; having ensured that the area was clear, he approached the doorway alone, was seen to bend over the package and was in the process of defusing it when it exploded. He was killed instantly.

GEORGE MEDAL

Watts, Hugh Edward MBE	Chief Inspector of Explosives at the Home Office. Bomb Disposal Terrorism.	August 1948
Henderson, Donald Victor MBE	Explosives Officer, Metropolitan Police. Bomb Disposal Terrorism.	December 1976
Biddle, Geoffrey William MBE	Explosives Officer, Metropolitan Police, Bomb Disposal Terrorism.	December 1976
Gurney, Peter Edwin Spencer MBE GM (a Bar to his GM)	Explosives Officer, Metropolitan Police, Bomb Disposal Terrorism.	August 1983
Howorth, Kenneth Robert (A posthumous award)	Explosives Officer, Metropolitan Police, Bomb Disposal Terrorism.	August 1983

MBE (GALLANTRY)

In addition to the above there have been three MBEs awarded for Gallantry:

Donald Victor Henderson
Geoffrey William Biddle
Peter Gurney GM

AWARDS TO CIVILIANS EMPLOYED BY THE MINISTRY OF SUPPLY, THE ROYAL ORDNANCE FACTORIES AND THE WOOLWICH ARSENAL

A brief account of the incident that resulted in the award of the George Cross recounts that on 22 February 1944, at a factory in Kirby, Liverpool, whilst the operators were filling fuzes, at 8.30am one fuze detonated, immediately involving a further 24 fuzes in the same way. Two people were killed and one badly injured. At the time of the incident some 12,000 fuzes were in the building. The explosion had been caused by a defective striker in the fuze and it was obvious that a similar defect could be present in other fuzes. It was decided that all fuzes in the building must be removed to a place of safety. Mr Bywater volunteered, with three other workers, and together they spent three days moving the fuzes from the wrecked factory. A total of 12,000 being moved, with a further 4,000 being suspected to have a similar defect. Mr Bywater's leadership enabled the dangerous task to be successfully completed.

GEORGE MEDAL

1940	Friend, Sidney Eric Preventing explosion, blazing ammunition trails and magazine	Woolwich
1941	Grant, James Limiting effects of factory explosion	Adeer, Ayrshire
1942	Scarr, Maurice Megnell Factory explosion	Aycliffe, Co. Durham
1943	Thomas, James Limiting effects of factory explosion	Aberporth, Cardiganshire
1944	Topping, William Limiting effects of factory explosion	Kirby, Liverpool
1944	Rawlings, Mark Victor Clearing scene and making safe after explosion	Kirby, Liverpool
1944	Murdock, James Shanks BEM Clearing scene and making safe after explosion	Kirby, Liverpool
1944	Panton, William James BEM Clearing scene and making safe after explosion	Kirby, Liverpool
1944	Edwards, Ray Thomas William Clearing scene and making safe after explosion	Kirby, Liverpool
1944	Fitzmaurice, William Laws BEM Clearing scene and making safe after explosion	Kirby, Liverpool
1945**	Bywater, Richard Samuel Clearing scene and making safe after explosion	Kirby, Liverpool

** Awarded George Cross September 1944 for incident on 22 February 1944 – the only civilian ever to be awarded both the George Cross and the George Medal.

MEMBERS OF THE RAOC WHO MADE THE SUPREME SACRIFICE ON EOD DUTIES, 1956-1996

Tragically, over the past years, 23 officers and soldiers have lost their lives undertaking bomb disposal operations. Until recently they had no special memorial. This has now changed. An appeal was started amongst serving and retired EOD operators and a design was selected. The sculpture was commissioned and the work was very quickly completed. Now, adjacent to the garrison church at Kineton, home of the School of Ammunition, there is a small walled garden, with the sculptured memorial.

SSgt	J A Culkin	25.09.56	Limassol (Cyprus)
SSgt	R Kirkby	31.07.58	Famagusta (Cyprus)
Sgt	C C Workman	28 08 67	Kowloon (Hong Kong)
Capt	D Stewartson	09.09.71	Castlerobin
WO2	C L Davies	24.11.71	Lurgan
SSgt	C R Cracknell	24.11.71	Belfast
Sgt	A S Butcher	15.03.72	Belfast
Maj	B C Calladene	29.03.72	Belfast
Capt	J Young	15.07.72	Forkill
WO2	W J Clark	03.08.72	Clady
Sgt	R E Hills	05.12.72	Lurgan
Capt	B S Gritten	21.06.73	Londonderry
SSgt	R K Beckett	30.08.73	Pettigoe (Omagh)
Capt	R Wilkinson	17.09.73	Birmingham (England)
SSgt	A N Brammah	18.02.74	Moybane (Bessbrook)
SSgt	V I Rose	07.11.74	Stewartson (Omagh)
WO2	J A Maddocks	02.12.74	Enniskillen (Omagh)
SSgt	J C Crawshaw	22.01.75	Holcombe Moor (England)
WO2	E Garside	17.07.75	Forkill (Bessbrook)
Cpl	C W Brown	09.01.77	Forkill (Bessbrook)
Sgt	M E Walsh	30.05.81	Drummully (Omagh)
WO2	M O'Neil	30.05.81	Newry (Bessbrook)
WO2	J R Howard	08.07.88	Belfast

'No doubt other branches of the army have more chance of dying on the battlefield, but the Army Ordnance Corps have shown how, by devotion to duty, and by nobly carrying out most responsible and arduous duties, to walk in the same way as all their comrades of other branches of the service.' – Field Marshal the Duke of Connaught, 1903.

INDEX